The House of Cure

Life within The Leicestershire Lunatic Asylum

Later to become The Leicestershire & Rutland
Lunatic Asylum in 1849

Then located at the current site of the
University of Leicester

Taken from the records of the Superintendents,
Medical Officers & Official Visitors
Collated By Diane Lockley

The House of Cure

Cover designed by Patrick Lockley

ISBN: 978-1-907540-43-1

Published June 2011

Printed and Published by Anchorprint Group Limited
www.anchorprint.co.uk

Acknowledgements

Firstly, my thanks go to the original superintendent's, medical officers both inside & outside the asylum and the clerks who carefully recorded details on the patients many years ago. My gratitude also specifically going to Dr Rothsay C. Stewart, one of the former Medical Superintendent's from 1895 until the time of the asylum's closure in 1908, who took some incredible photographs.

Secondly, my thanks must go to Adam Goodwin at The Record Office for Leicestershire, Leicester & Rutland at Wigston Magna *(ROLLR)*. He was in charge of collecting & collating all the records and getting them ready for Record Office access, for the general public. He also gave his precious time, to read through the 'House of Cure', giving many exceptionally valuable comments & suggestions. I must also thank other members of Record Office staff who had to fetch the massive old bound case books which often left them with marks on their otherwise spick & span apparel. With thanks also going to Alex Cave the University of Leicester Archivist who carefully selected any illustrative records that are still held within the University of Leicester Records.

Thirdly, I thank Kathleen Bumstead (now deceased) my history lecturer & personal tutor at Ripon College of Education in Yorkshire. From the very beginnings she motivated my fascination with historical records. Because of her, I enjoyed spending days down in the vaults in Yorkshire Record Offices with dusty records. She was the lady who inspired my initial reaction of absolute amazement, when I first opened one of the Case Books of the Leicestershire County Asylum. Initially, I used them to research the history of handicap within Leicestershire children & published a leaflet entitled 'Whether or If'.

Finally, my gratitude goes to Tony, Nathaniel and Patrick for the support that they have given throughout the production of this publication including Moby the dog.

This book is dedicated to my mother Barbara Marie Davies who was at one time a patient of the Warwickshire Asylum at Hatton.

'I don't know what you want me here for, you must all be mad…
I don't want anybody to take care of me, I can take care of myself."

Case Book Entry for Edward who was originally
a confectioner from London. (196/4250)

'..and the inroads that wretchedness had made upon a once well ordered mind'.

Henry a clerk from Ketton (185/620)

'..complains that she is being ill-treated by the writer'.

Matilda a grocer's wife from Market Harborough (197/4617)

Any inclusions are taken as written in the actual records

Etching of the Leicestershire & Rutland Lunatic Asylum January 1890 - By James Murray (the only former patient whose full name is given throughout this publication). Courtesy of University of Leicester Archives ULA/IMA2/2.

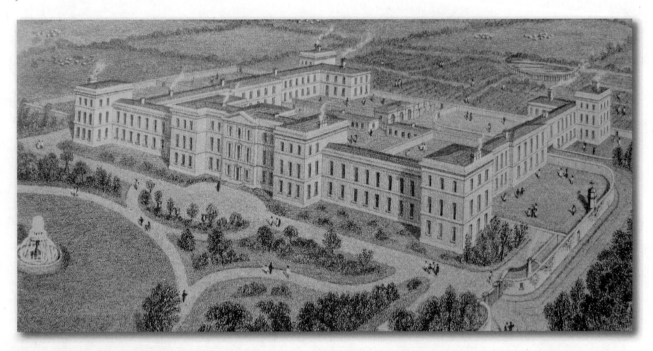

Early Drawing Of The Asylum In 1849 By T Wilson is reproduced from an engraving by H Adlard to be used in Annual Reports.

Courtesy of University of Leicester Archives.

Contents

(Various individual photographs are taken from the later Case Notes Records of patients who recovered after treatment in the Leicestershire & Rutland Lunatic Asylum. DE3533-203-205-206 Individual identities have been withheld. Courtesy of the Record Office for Leicestershire, Leicester & Rutland at Wigston Magna - *ROLLR*).

Aerial photograph of the Fielding Johnson Building taken during the early 1930 FG1/3/96. Courtesy of University of Leicester Archives.

Glossary of terms used within this publication

Apoplexy: Paralysis due to a stroke.

Debility: Lack of movement or staying in bed.

Dementia: Decay or obliteration of the intellectual faculties.

Erysipelas: Contagious skin disease due to streptococci with vesicular & bulbous lesions.

Feeble-mined: Obsolete term for mental retardation and mental handicap.

General Paralysis of the insane: A syndrome of madness & weakness occurring in tertiary syphilis.

Hysteria: A real disease with physical symptoms that cannot be attributed to any underlying physical cause.

Idiot: Obsolete term for a person of extremely low intelligence, whose intellectual faculties have never been developed, having a mental age of less than 3 years old.

Imbecile: Obsolete term for a person of the second order of mental retardation, above the level of idiocy, having a mental age of seven or eight years.

Insanity: A term for any form of mental illness which renders a person incapable of acting in accordance with the legal & conventional standards of the times.

Lunacy & Lunatic: Obsolete term for a mentally ill person originally derived by a supposed connection between mental illness & the moon.

Melancholia: A mental condition characterised by great depression of spirits & gloomy foreboding.

Mania: A type of effective disorder characterised by euphoric mood excessive activity & talkativeness, impaired judgement, affecting all the operations of the brain.

Phthisis: Chronic wasting away or another name for tuberculosis.

Puerperal fever: Elevated temperature after giving birth to an infant.

RO: An abbreviation used for Relieving Officer.

Softening of the brain: Result of a stroke or a haemorrhage in the brain, with the end result of the tissue softening in that area.

Photograph of front gardens.
Courtesy of University of Leicester Archives ULA/FG1/3/10.

Introduction

"There they stand, isolated, majestic, imperious, brooded over by the gigantic water-tower and chimney combined, rising unmistakable and daunting out of the countryside – the asylum which our forefathers built with such immense solidity."

Enoch Powell, Minister if Health 1961

The Leicestershire County Lunatic Asylum was completed in 1837 at a cost of £17.948.19s 1d. (In 1849 it was to become the Leicestershire & Rutland Lunatic Asylum). The Counties Asylum Act of 1808 resulted in several new county asylums being built. Nottinghamshire Asylum was the first to be built in 1810, followed by Bedford (1812), Norfolk at Thorpe (1814), Lancaster (1816), Stafford (1818), West Riding of Yorkshire at Wakefield (1818), Cornwall at Bodmin (1820), Lincolnshire (1820) and Gloucestershire (1823). The Leicestershireshire Asylum was one of another eight, which opened later.[1]

The new Leicestershire Asylum, was an exceptionally forward thinking institution, opening its doors to patients for the first time on 10th May 1837 taking over from the smaller Leicester Infirmary Asylum, which had opened 16th April 1794, and had been a three-storey block of cells for the inmates, also with accommodation for the keepers. (For the rest of this publication the Asylum will be given its eventual full name which was to include Rutland.) There were just 12 patients admitted on the first day, the first recorded being a Mary from Shepshed, but there were initially spaces for 104 patients. The new Asylum was sited in the countryside, on a hill, near to Leicester racecourse & was surrounded by parkland & agricultural land, with just one cottage getting in the way of what was otherwise a completely rural landscape. James Murray, an architectural surveyor, who was once a patient at the asylum, shows in his engraving, the bird's eye view of the County Asylum in its countryside setting in 1891.[2] The new Asylum was positioned on what is now the current site of the University of Leicester. The Fielding Johnson building and the Medical Superintendent's house are the only two buildings from the original asylum that are still standing.

The Admission Registers (surviving from 1837), the Case Books (surviving as records from January 1845), the Superintendent's Journals from April 1871 to January 1912), two Charity patients' case books, two Medical Journals & the reports of the Official visitors were all used to gather information on what life was like within the County Asylum, together with details of the lives outside (mentioned in the case books) that had resulted in the many necessary admissions. The Case Books are generally about the Pauper patients or the patients transferring to & from Charity status. This study has little or no information on how it was for the 'Independent' patients except for one Medical Journal & unless certain details are recorded in the Superintendent's journals, with no mention of patient status. Within the records, especially the volumes of case notes, there were vast quantities to read & also not all of the records have survived. Once admitted many of the entries could be very repetitive reaffirmations of the patient's current state of health, but a change of ink & handwriting style usually implied that something different had taken place, or the writer was going to be slightly more open, outspoken or elaborate than usual. On exceptionally rare occasions, the content of the records, do appear rather incredulous, but they have been taken as written. This study is about the staff & their

---

1   Leicestershire's Lunatics – The Institutional care of Leicester shire's Lunatics during the Nineteenth Century H G Orme W H Brock Leicestershire Museums & Art Galleries 1987 ISBN 085022 227 3.

2   An engraving by James Murray a patient (University of Leicester Archives). See introductory illustration.

patients, who were individuals, often completely involuntarily spending a significant part of their existence certified away from their normal lives: This study is not essentially about the walls within which many successfully found a cure. There are some rough totals & approximate statistics but this compilation is essentially about individual people & not about patients whose colourful & very significant individual identity or unique experiences are lost within generalised groups. It is hoped that readers do not tire of sentences, paragraphs and pages full of phrases like - Sarah the bible reader from Shepshed (197/4614), Mark Anthony (197/4629) the warehouseman from Loughborough or Harry (197/4637) the timber agent from Syston, because this is who they actually were – very real people who were desperately mentally ill enough, to be in need of admission to an asylum. The patients have been recorded in a way that has enabled them to still remain, to this day, essentially anonymous, (with just one exception James Murray the draughtsman whose outstanding drawing is shown within this publication). The earliest chapters because they concentrate on the admission process and the reason for admission may make life, in the asylum, appear rather bleak: The later sections, which concentrate on treatments do take us into 'The House of Cure'.

My own misconception that mentally ill individuals arrived, at times hidden in carriages, often in restraints, to spend the rest of their lives behind locked asylum doors, was soon cast aside.

> 'Nevertheless on the 2nd inst in the afternoon, Not one male patient was in bed, in the wards, or even in the airing courts – That is every individual male patient was free & beyond lock & key – and it may be doubted whether this ever occurred before in any Asylum.' June 1885 [3]

The records emphasize that from its very beginnings, the Leicestershire Asylum was a very progressive institution & was always intended to be a 'House of Cure'. There was at last a place for them: There was place for those with severe mental illness or for those with congenital defects who could no longer cope or be coped with.

Photographs of Male Patients. Asylum Casebooks courtesy of ROLLR.

---

3   Superintendent's Journal DE3533-86

The need for Admission - The Case Books & The Admission Process

The extensive patient Case Book records remain, still found within County Records from 2nd January 1845 to February 1908. Each of the 26 Case Books contained information on between 150 to 300 admissions. The Case Books had double (or later on quadruple) pages for an incoming patient, which almost always included an entry number, Christian & surnames, age, place of abode, the closest relative or named contact (usually with their address), occupation, marital status, number of children, the date of admission, the supposed reason for onset & a brief diagnosis. Certain other sections required various pieces of information, but the doctors or clerks, did not always have the necessary details in order to complete all these sections. A couple of men admitted as wanderers, were actually admitted as complete Mr 'X's as nobody knew who they were or where they came from, including themselves - the information boxes for these patients were a tragic accumulation of 'not known'. For one of these patients (203/6196) who was admitted on 8th November 1900, for whom absolutely 'nothing was known of him', including his Christian name or surname. He said he was a horse dealer called Jesse but this could not be verified. Another patient (203/6095) was problematical because he offered two completely different names and previous abode addresses – John from Newcastle Under Lyme or Robert from Levenshulme Manchester. The officer at the time of admission really makes his point with a patient named John from Leicester, who is admitted with very little information: -

> 'The previous history of the patient like that of most others is wrought in mystery, for the reasons so frequently assigned before and it is much to be regretted, that some more compulsory means are not adopted by legal enactment, to remedy so important a deficiency in the furnishing of information essentially useful in the treatment of the case and most invaluable in a statistical point of view.' (185/730)

In the later years of the asylum identification with the use of photographs became a 'god send': -

> 'Letter from Berrywood, Northampton enclosing a photograph of this man, who was admitted there under the name of Alfred ....'. (204/37).

In contrast to those patients where there was little or no information on them, there were those like Henry a railway labourer who had the required information, but had no inclination to give it: -

> 'Will not answer to his name - says he never had any name - that he is dead - never was alive - never was born - never married - never had any children - that he is nothing - & never came from anywhere.' (204/77)

A labourer from Oakham, who had been traumatised by the death of his daughter who had drowned herself with her 8 month old daughter was obviously quite distraught & not perhaps keen on maintaining his identity for when asked his name he replied that: -

> 'I have none & if you find one, you can bring it along.' (206/40)

The layout of the pages in the case books was slightly altered as the books became complete with incoming patients and newly printed books with different inclusive columns were commenced. If the pages became complete, then any follow up information was added on another patient's page who had either been cured quite quickly, had died relatively soon, or whose condition did not require constant detailed entries. Priority appeared to be given to any clinical event related to each patient, such as bodily damage as the result of suicidal attempts, accidents, attacks, fevers, digestive system problems, heart or lung conditions and epileptic convulsions, to name but a few. To take just one example Clara from Shardlow,

> 'She has this afternoon severely bruised and slightly lacerated her hand, fore-arm and elbow in the washing machine'. (202/5860)

Details of the patient's mental condition was obviously also an appropriate entry, with the more negative extremes, such as padded rooms, forced feeding, or for some the continuing major delusions, always finding a place within the entries, together with how the patient was or was not able to occupy themselves within an asylum day. The mental state, was not otherwise always apparently viewed as the most imperative entry.

2 of the 26 asylum case books held at the Leicestershire County Record Office. Courtesy of ROLLR.

This precedence to the entry of the clinical details surely emphasises just how much of a hospital the County Lunatic Asylum was. As well as the treatment of mental illness, many other medical things were continually happening. It was essential that the asylum was always a hospital too, for a high number of patients were not just mentally ill they were physically ill to.

There are two medical journals surviving from the 1870's, which included the names of the patients that were admitted that week, those who had died since the last entry, and patients under medical treatment (for what if any bodily disorder) & the entries being divided into columns for males & females. At times just the patients' specific forms of mental illness was recorded such as John (193/3367) with mania & Thomas (193/3130) with melancholia. Mental illness did not of course prevent patients from developing other bodily conditions & the following medical complaints are all entries within the medical treatment books - Abscesses, anaemia, amenorrhoea, amputations, anthrax, apoplexy, asthma, bed sores, black eyes, bronchitis, bruises, burns & scalds, bursitis, cancer of various body parts, carbuncles, colic, conjunctivitis, consumption, corneas, cystitis, delirium tremors, derangements (hepatic), diarrhoea, diseases of various body parts (with frequent mention of diseased brains, hearts & lungs) dislocations, dropsy, dyspepsia, epilepsy, erysipelas, erythema, eczema, excitement, exhaustion, fever, gangrene, gout, haematuria, haemoptysis, haemorrhoids, hemiplegia, hernias, icterus, impetigo, inflammations, injuries & wounds to various body parts, insomnia, jaundice, lumbago, oedemas, ophthalmia, orchitis, palpitations, paralysis, phthisis, pneumonia, prolapsed ani, prostatic enlargements, psoriasis, puerperal complaints, refusal of food, retention of urine, rheumatism, scrofula, shingles, tonsillitis, tumours, ulcers, urticaria, varicose veins, venereal disease, whitlows & worms.

The busiest week in these still found medical records (of just two books) was 12th Feb 1877 when 13 Male patients & 15 female patients were specifically under medical treatment for cerebral disease, debility, dementia, diarrhoea, epilepsy, erythema, excision of phalanx, paralysis, icterus, contagious impetigo, mania, melancholia, rheumatism & wounds to a leg. Can it be assumed that these patients were receiving specific medicines & this is why they were distinctively selected, as there were hundreds of other patients receiving treatment in February 1877? Incidentally, there were three cases recorded of anthrax in the two surviving medical records books, none of them actually dying from that condition. These were John a railway signalman, Frances an elderly housewife and Robert a framework knitter from Fleckney. Robert the knitter appeared to be the only one who had any occupational link with the disease that gained itself the nickname 'wool sorter's disease'. Industrial anthrax was once rife in the 1840's, amongst wool sorters who had contracted the disease via contaminated spores from imported alpaca & angora. As well as all these certain medical complications to the asylum routine several babies were also delivered.

From its very beginnings it is continually evident that the main aim of the new institution was to cure and not to detain. *'A HOUSE OF CURE & NOT A HOUSE OF DETENTION'.*[4] The definition of the word 'asylum' continues to this day to denote 'safety'. Many if they had not been in the Leicester Infirmary Asylum, had been waiting for years for an appropriate treatment for their condition. Some had had private attendants; some had been in small private asylums or had been inmates in small alms houses or more usually Work Houses. If one patient was perhaps a 'sure cure' at the time of admission, then it had to be Kate (195/4094) a road surveyor's daughter from Foxton, whose condition on entry was recorded as 'Convalescing from mania', so she was perhaps fortunate as being already on the mend.

---

4   Committee of Visitors Prefatory Remarks Rules 1849.

Once the new asylum doors were open then there were of course continuous ongoing admissions. The new patients would be drawn in from the busy town streets, the more centralised village environments or the remote rural locations. The reasons for these new admissions, who came from every type of environment, included the socially unacceptable use of restraints within a family or work based household, threats of suicide, the mentally unsound wanderers, persons manifesting dangerous behaviours, individuals who were not under proper care or control and mentally ill patients who had become or were also often quite desperately physically ill too. Several clinically ill patients were brought in from hospitals because their behaviours had become dangerously unmanageable in that environment.

In the later case books patients were photographed soon after admission. The photographic apparatus had been purchased in London in February 1893. When John (199/5007) a peddler was being photographed he expressed a strong desire that his photos should not be spread about over the country, as everyone would know him. Mary (203/6113) a laundress was worried the image would be used to her detriment and Eleanor (202/5853) from Atherstone believed that it was the 'Almighty' himself who had photographed her. A few were so ill at the time of admission that their photographic record had to be taken when they were actually dead, as was the case for Richard a (203/6169) general labourer from Shepshed. Agnes (210/1) could not be photographed at the time of admission, as she was too prostrate & her image also had to be taken after her death, eight days later.

Usually an area Relieving Officer would visit the patient, in their pre-admission residence, to verify the need for admission. His paper records gave the asylum doctors information on the incoming patient. It was not always easy to assess those who may have been about to become an asylum patient. We have an example of James Olderwood, the Relieving Officer for Oakham, who had problems weighing up the possibility of a Maria (210-45) becoming a patient, as she tried to bar his entrance to her abode by throwing a knife at him. A lady from the Rifle Range Road in Ashby, was visited to be assessed by the Relieving Officer (212/20), and during his assessment caused him much annoyance: -

'She kept breaking out in singing in a piercing voice which was most trying to listen to.'

One wonders how her family, who shared a home with her, coped with, what for them could have threatened to be continuous, discordant musical accompaniment. Jane from Stamford (212/66) was obviously quite confused when the 'RO' (an abbreviation frequently used for the Relieving Officer in the asylum records) came to visit as: -

'Thinks that I (whom she knows well) am a traveller from Stamford.'

When visiting Louisa (212/78) from Easton the Relieving Officer had to suffer some quite uncomplimentary comments: -

'She told me I was only fit to beat a big drum outside & sirens.'

Their local doctors had treated many of the patients previously at home. Elizabeth (185/757) from Loughborough is recorded as: -

'Gross delusions on the subject of religion - under the influence of feelings, wrought to a pitch of frenzy - she has been under medical treatment but not subjected to personal restraint.'

Keeping those with serious mental afflictions safe was not an easy task for their carers. Amongst the many admissions were 'idiots' & 'imbeciles', who had arrived from various environments. Emma (186/1091) an idiot from Leicester, admitted in June 1850, had been kept in a dark cellar, chained to a post and was the fear and tenor of her neighbourhood. Admissions of those with some form of congenital defect were frequently the result of a death within households. Thomas (189/2135) an imbecile, had been up to the age of 52, living with his mother. In complete contrast to Thomas's history, Walter's (201/5491) mother left for America immediately after his birth in 1844. Grandparents often took on extremely significant roles. Lydia (212/72) an illegitimate imbecile had been virtually brought up by her grandfather & did get employment as a domestic servant for a time. She was ultimately placed in Shardlow Workhouse because she was so unmanageable, but her grandfather did have her out of the workhouse when he was able to. Sometimes the chore of looking after grandchildren (who were at times orphans) became too much for grandparents to deal with. Aunts, uncles, sisters and brothers, nephews, nieces & cousins also withheld the family duties and did their best when required to care for their handicapped blood relative. Many 'idiots' and 'imbeciles' were epileptic too and a few of those admitted were multiply handicapped, such as young Frederick from Knighton: -

> 'The patient is completely unable either to walk- speak or feed himself, he is obliged to be fed with a spoon of the attendant and passes both faeces & urine apparently without consciousness.' (193/3175)

It is evident from the profound nature of handicaps as extensive as Frederick's, that many family households would have found it exceptionally difficult to care for siblings afflicted with such a degree of major disabilities. Especially, those such as the mother Emma (211/89) from Overseal who had 16 children in all to care for & her supposed cause of mental illness was looking after an idiot daughter. Due to a lack of resources or scarcity of actual time to give effective care, some parents were forced to resort to the absolute basics. The daily family life must have been thwarted; dealing with the doubly incontinent and the need to keep certain family members reasonably clean, together with their clothes, their bedding & floors. Young John (195/3778) from Thorpe Satchville is quoted, 'as obeying the call of nature just like an animal at any time or place'. One of the idiot male patients was admitted wearing female clothes, which is how he had been dressed for some time. Female clothes for a not fully 'toileting aware' males may have had the potential to lower the laundry pile? (193/3117)

It was not just the very young & congenitally handicapped that instilled extensive levels of care from immediate household members. Families were again, potentially the strongest link when it came to supporting other members of their clan, who were struggling to maintain a relatively normal life pattern. Relatives generally felt obliged to step in & help or to take over, when the nearest & dearest could no longer take proper care of themselves or were behaving problematically. A groom's wife Emma (211/52) was just one lady from High Street, Castle Donington, who was not able to take care of herself or fit to be at large in her community. Some blood relations were quite empathic to struggling members of their family. Phoebe's (210/138) husband from Markfield felt that his wife was just too fond of their children & did not have sufficient rest from looking after them. Elizabeth's (210/148) husband Stephen was very obviously devoted to her, for he accompanied her to the asylum on her admission. He had gone completely blind in one eye and was very partially sighted in the other; so one can only wonder how he (having no children) was going to manage when he returned home. An elderly lady from Wigston Magna, was taken from her previous home in Markfield by her daughter, because she was no longer able to take proper care of herself. Unfortunately, the same Mary (211/12) kept wandering off to the local Wigston railway station, in an attempt to return, to what she must have felt was her home. Sometimes husbands & wives were both patients within the asylum, as was the case for Samuel (189/2201) & Elizabeth (189/2103). John (205/26) from Asfordby's wife was also a patient but he did not wish to see her believing that they were better apart. Sometimes, family members were actually admitted on the same day to the asylum, as was the case with Emma (211/89) & Mary Ann (211/90) her idiot daughter admitted in February 1905. Ann from Walcot's brother William (192/2852) was also a patient: -

> 'She frequently enquires about her brother whom she has seen on several occasions at chapel and at the dancing.' (192/2912)

When outside attempts to care were no longer sufficient, family members became inmates of the asylum. These new patients were often from the very beginning, patients 'of' the asylum, not necessarily always patients 'in'. It must be recognised from the very outset, that many of the patients were allowed outside for various social and occupational activities: they were not necessarily 'forever in'. Individuals of course had to be brought in to actually become patients. Journeys in the 19th Century could be quite daunting for those who were in good health, so what would the journeys have been like for those that were very noticeably mentally & or physically unwell? Considerable numbers of patients were transported on what could have been quite traumatic journeys, so that their admission would comply with their original place of settlement and who was to fund the treatment. Sarah from Castle Donington had been in asylums in Hereford & Nottingham, but as the following case book entry emphasises she was quite upset by being on the move again in October 1849: -

> 'The Patient's mind latterly has been a good deal harassed in consequence of a contemplated removal from Leicester to Derby where she was a few days ago, the journey and its object seem together to have completely upset her and also to have been the exciting cause of an attack.' (186/1007)

Frederick (204/7) a messenger from Mount St Bernards Abbey, had absolutely no recollection of his journey the day before his admission & had therefore perhaps had had a comfortable and non-eventful trip. Joseph (203/6128) a hosier from Enderby, had been anxious to come to the Asylum, as he believed that the Queen had actually wished it. At times the distance between 'A' and 'B' was quite considerable. Ann (190/2540) a farmer's daughter from Twycross had been taken ill at a lodging house in Rhyll, where she had broken glass and several items of furniture. A lady who travelled one of the longest distances in 1882, was an Eliza aged 35 with primary dementia, who had originated from Staunton Harold, before she had gone abroad with her husband: -

> 'She has been married 12 years, most of which time she has spent abroad with her husband in Java, India, Sicily & other places. It is supposed that her husband put her on the packet at Sicily for France and then left her. She was brought to England 8 weeks ago by a nurse from an asylum at Marseilles where she had been either 6 weeks or months.' (196/4285)

Another Roman Catholic lady from Great Bowden (196/4359) had been taken care of at a convent in France and expressed a wish to return to a French convent. The place of abode for others within the Case Books was recorded as Ballaghadarren (County Down) Belfast, Birkenhead, Birmingham, Braintree, Bristol, Cambridge, Coventry, Croydon, Denmark, Derby, Dublin, Grantham, Halifax, Leeds, Lincoln, Liverpool, London, Manchester, Newcastle on Tyne, Northampton, North Wales, Nottingham, Rugby, Salford, Sheffield, Somerset, Stockport, Surrey and Tamworth. Some patients had obviously found it difficult having to work away from home. Donald (218/349) from West Street in Leicester had developed chronic mania, perhaps as a result of being apprenticed to the sea & sailing as far as Sydney. Jennie (212/149) who was found to be chargeable to Barrow, had her residence at the time of admission in July 1908 given as the 'SS Victorian in Liverpool'. She had been out to Canada & must have been taken ill on the return journey as she was taken from the ship to Liverpool Workhouse & then certified insane whilst an inmate there. Ambrose (201/5414) from Surrey had developed simple mania two weeks after arriving to work as a carpenter at the Ratcliffe Roman Catholic College. A groom from Germany named Emil (204/74) developed melancholia, due in part to being horrendously teased by the vicar from Birstall's servants. He was eventually transferred to the care of the Relieving Officer and sent back to Germany in 1905. Even patients coming from within Leicestershire itself could have had some distance to travel.

Regardless of where they were coming from, the patients had completely individual views on their forthcoming admission. Thomas (195/3973) a gardener from Houghton on the Hill had no desire to live & anticipated that the rough treatment he was expecting to receive within the asylum, would soon finish him off anyway. Lois (212/49) from Nottingham Road in Loughborough told the 'RO' that if she had known before that she was coming to the asylum, she would have drowned herself. Mary Ann who had been admitted from Loughborough Police Station, believed that she was coming to the asylum to be shot & kept telling the Relieving Officer that,

> 'Police Superintendent Agar had wired to say, that she was innocent & that she was to be taken back to Loughborough.' (211/115)

On learning of his imminent asylum admission, George (205/64) a factory hand, decided that he must commit suicide beforehand. William ((204/111) from Oakham believed he had been sent to the asylum for betraying the Masonic Passwords. Another William (205/21) from Markfield believed that his visit to the Asylum served the purpose of collecting his brother from there. Alowzo (204/43) a Royal Marine believed that he was going to the asylum to pick up his uniform & equipment. A licensed victualler from Baxter Gate Loughborough named Henry (192/2848) thought he was going to have a Turkish bath and not to be admitted to an asylum. A railway labourer transferred from Rainhill in Lancashire in 1890, believed he had come to get a job paving the ship canal and the asylum was the Canal Offices. (199/5081) Sarah (197/4412) from Prestwold actually believed that she was a nurse and consequentially greatly resented being treated as just a patient. Catherine was: -

> 'Very full of complaints at being kept here. She says she will bring actions against all the guardians for allowing her to be deprived of her liberty'. (192/2871)

Many incoming patients did not want to be manhandled. Even with limbs firmly secured, it could still take four to six men to manoeuvre certain patients both male & female to the asylum. Jane (195/3780) from Barlestone, aged 22 had to be brought in, tied down in a tented wagon. Charles (205/144) a farm labourer from Nanpantan, declared 'that even six men would not bring him in'. Several patients had to arrive in a strait waistcoat, otherwise admitting them without injuries would have been exceedingly difficult, and any bruises on admission were always meticulously recorded. Young Beatrice (197/4799) from Claybrooke Magna required both the strait waistcoat and metallic foot manacles. One new admission (187/1598) arrived with several bruises about his body apparently caused by the tightness with which a strait waistcoat had been fastened. Susannah from Great Glenn: -

> 'Really took against her husband & nurse - said when brought here that a trap had been laid for her.' (211/108)

It was Minnie's second admission & when learning she was returning to the asylum: -

> 'She was very violent, yelled murder all the way & tore down the lining of the cab inside.' (211/48)

At times the admission was quite traumatic for all involved, sometimes sadly necessitating the immediate use of a padded room. Sarah (194/3417) from Rutland was one of several patients, placed in a padded room after being admitted in December 1873.

Elizabeth (200/5331) from Blackfordby had behaviour, which was not quite so problematical on admission, for she only jumped on the weighing machine and just would not stand still to be weighed. Initially, most patients arrived by horse & carriage but eventually, the new railway lines were more frequently used as a form of transport to & from the asylum. Elizabeth (210/47) from Kegworth, admitted in October 1901 named all the railway stations correctly on the way. Jane (210/37) from Knossington declared that she had arrived by 'fast train'. A wheelwright from Kegworth (205/78) became violent on the train to Leicester and the police had to be called to the station to assist with his admission. Many came with no problems at all, but that was often tragically because they had absolutely no idea at that time of who they were, where they were, let alone where they were actually going. Samuel (201/5469) from Cropston in November 1893 & William (201/5574) from Thurmaston North in December 1894 both likened the County Asylum to the 'Bastille'. A grocer's assistant John declared: -

> 'That he is going out and never coming back: that we are all rogues and vagabonds.' (217CCB229)

Isaac (201/5565) from Hinckley in comparison likened the same Institution to the 'second Eden'. Charles (196/4418) an artist from Aylestone Park had quite an unusual pattern of admittance, as when he thought that he was being taken to the asylum, he ran away for at least 50 miles and enlisted twice. His determination not to be admitted becomes quite understandable, when a later casebook record states that ultimately his admission was found to be illegal, with details being returned to the commissioners declaring he was 'not insane'.

Once the doors were opened then new patients would arrive usually only on Wednesdays or Saturdays generally between 11.00 am and 2.00 pm. Patients kept arriving & by 1867 the asylum was housing about seventy more than the 342 it was designed for. After a time the grand huge stylish architecture of the asylum buildings began to falter under the mounting weight of the numbers inside.' In the 1890s there were over a hundred more residents registered, than actual official places.

The new patients arrived throughout the seasons of winter, spring, summer & autumn. It was hardly a case of seasonal adjustment depression being of high occurrence in the 19th Century, for if we were to go by the month of admission, the figures were just as high in summer and spring as they were in autumn or winter. The figures should be viewed as approximate, but they can be ranked in the following monthly order – January 525 admissions, February 489 admissions, March 574 admissions, April 531 admissions, May 630 admissions, June 551 admissions, July 621 admissions, August 571 admissions, September 495 admissions, October 481 admissions, November 485 admissions and December 526 admissions.

Admission to the Asylum required an obligatory medical certificate, with that piece of paper usually giving the asylum medical officer the basic very necessary information of the incoming patient. John (204/30) a joiner from Loughborough was exceedingly anxious about what the doctors had put in the certificate about him. Any irregularities with the certificate often called for the patient's admission being refused and them having to be readmitted later (sometimes the same day) when the paper work was correct. Owing to gross informalities in his certificate John (191/2636) from Staunton Harold was just one who had to be immediately discharged. Minnie (211/20) from Leicester Workhouse arrived at the asylum on the evening of September 25th 1903 all by herself & wanted to be admitted as a patient. She declared that the necessary papers had been signed the day before at Ashby (which was actually the case). She was though sent down to the Leicester Workhouse, where she attempted suicide the same evening. She did eventually acquire her asylum placement in November of the same year. There were usually one or two admissions a day and on some days none at all. One of the busiest days for the County Asylum appears to have been 11th September 1846 when 17 new patients were admitted, almost all of them, as a transfer from Haydock Lodge, a private asylum for the restoration & cure of the insane, sited near St Helens in Merseyside. (Six of these individuals had initially been patients at the County Asylum and were being brought back from Merseyside to their former treatment site).

At the time of admission the doctor was determined to make an accurate assessment of each & every patient's both physical & mental condition. He did not just busily scribe: He also listened to what the patients had to tell him. At times the words & phrases he heard were quite delusionally absurd but he still wrote down the details. Several new admissions were in too poor a state of health to be able to communicate. Some were either too confused or had withdrawn into themselves so deeply, to be able to answer, even simple questions. Ellen from Morcott near Uppingham, who was admitted suffering from dementia is recorded as: -

'She cannot tell me the day of the week or month - nor what she has eaten for the last meal.' (210/131)

A few new arrivals had extremely limited communication skills, which would have made any opportunity to comment on their current mental state on admission virtually impossible. Sarah from Cross Street in Oakham, admitted suffering from melancholia, was obviously not completely out of her mind, and was able to continually make a quite rational statement: -

'What does it mean' 'Am I a bad case' 'Oh let me go home'. (203/6154)

Some patients had the language skills but they were not able to readily communicate. Mary (186/1044) from Gaddesby was recorded as not having spoken a word since her admission. Several who did speak, did so in barely audible tones. Charles (205/33) a groom's articulation was so impaired that it was practically quite unintelligible. An innkeeper from Keyworth admitted due to intemperance was quite incommunicative when admitted: -

'At present the want of coordinating power in the muscles engaged in articulation is most marked on admission he could scarcely utter a sentence.' (195/3908)

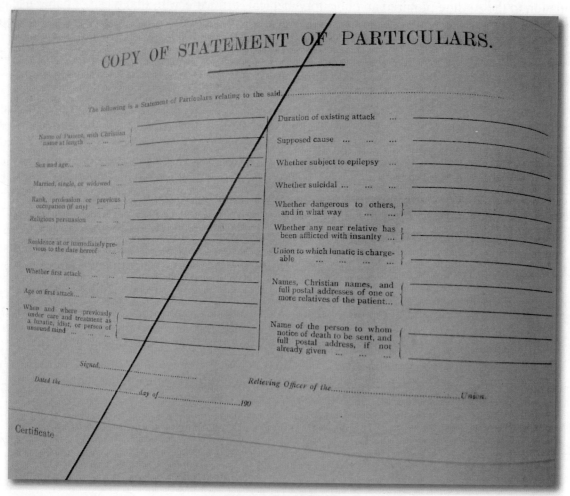

Photograph of an unused entry sheet within one of the Asylum case books. Courtesy of ROLLR.

Henry (202/5874) was difficult to understand because of his constant stammering. William (198/4882) an imbecile from Ullesthorpe could not answer a question rationally & in reply to most questions he either whistled or called out 'Mamma'. Communicating could be complex enough when trying to converse in English but Charles (197/4444) who worked with plaster at Loughborough had spent a large proportion of his life in France, so he talked in a very incoherent manner, in a mixture of broken English & French. Martha (193/3140) from Clay Cross was unable to speak more than a few monosyllables intelligently & made most of her wants known by signing. Maria (196/4295) from South Kilworth was recorded as being totally deaf and even though she was eventually happy & contented working in the laundry, her imperfect articulation, rendered any conversation extremely tedious & unsatisfactory. Some who did converse with members of staff would ramble not sticking to the point. Samuel (192/3053) a huntsman from Kirby Mallory sometimes gave answers completely foreign to the subject in hand. Sarah (198/4904) a former domestic 'used the word "bloody" really frequently, 'interpolating it almost between every second or third word'. A few patients had the same answer to absolutely any question like a Mary (201/5573) from Shenton near to Nuneaton: -

"When can I go home?"

Others would offer plenty of information, but the quality of their speech was not always appreciated, as was the case for Martha from Ullesthorpe: -

'She wanders from one subject to another intermixing her conversation with blasphemy.' (212/45)

Patients during admission must have had some sort of chance to get to know one another, as a Charles (204/95) from Hinckley was anxious to work at the farm with another man also from Hinckley, who had been admitted on the same day as him. They had perhaps either journeyed together to the asylum or had been seated in close proximity to one another, waiting to be assigned a ward number. There was separate accommodation for the charity & independent patients, but the case books do at times include some charity patients who have switched to or from the status of pauper. There was also almost certainly separate accommodation for the 'incurable' & 'curable as the legislation of 1845 would have eventually made it illegal to have both groups together. Throughout the case books there is noticeable reference of certain patients being reclassified within the status of 'chronic'. The liability of transfer from the aforementioned different types of accommodation apparently played a major role in the reward & punishment aspects of the treatment.

The accommodation for men & women was definitely separate. From the layout of the surviving Fielding Johnson building it can be seen that the asylum was of the "corridor" type (see photographs of wards) consisting of a series of corridors with wards and other rooms opening of them, connected together in wings at right angles to one another. The corridors were also evidently used as day rooms. A severe lack of space led to the erection of wooden buildings, which earned themselves the nickname of the 'huts'.

There were actually three admissions on Christmas Day – Richard (186/1139) a basket maker from Castle Donington in 1850, Joshua (193/3351) a labourer from Thurlaston in 1872 & Edward (202/5903) a hairdresser from Loughborough in 1897. One of the sadder admissions on Christmas Eve was seven-year-old Frederick (193/3175) from Knighton. There were just over seven thousand admissions in all to the County Asylum between May 1837 & September 1908. Ultimately, for many patients it was not the first admission. Over six hundred & thirty patients had more than one admission with one hundred and twelve being subsequently readmitted within a year of their first admission. In complete contrast, William (217/141) an idiot's first admission was in September 1838, he had his return admission from Broughton Astley, 39 years later in December 1877. Eleven other imbeciles & one other idiot were readmitted to the asylum. Six of those mentally handicapped patients were just transferred to & from their place of settlement workhouse to the asylum again. Just one imbecile William (202/5826) was readmitted twice and was said to have 'visions of Broadmoor looming up'. The rest of the readmitted idiots & imbeciles had just experienced one readmission. The average expectation period for readmission of all patients regardless of mental ability would be approximately six years. Not forgetting several blocks of data is missing, from found records, five hundred & four individuals were admitted twice, one hundred & one patients 3 times, thirty one patients 4 times, eleven patients 5 times, three patients 6 times and four patients 7 times. Jane (185/761) from Great Easton, Rebecca from Loughborough and Ann (191/2655) from Woodthorpe all came back for treatment 8 times. Thomas (204/51) a pork butcher from Newbold is recorded as having been previously admitted 11 times (this is written in the casebooks but does not coincide with the case book records admissions). Sometimes the readmissions were quite close together with Elizabeth (193/3186) from Burton Overy being readmitted 15 times but she did not eventually die in the asylum.

For several patients it may have been their first admission to the Leicestershire & Rutland County Asylum but it was not their first admission to an asylum. Certain incoming individuals had been previously treated at various asylums. At times 'private asylum' is included within their records, with no information of exactly where. The other asylums listed in Great Britain, where patients had been previously sited included Abington Abbey, Aldershot, Bedford, Berrisford, Northampton (Berrywood & St Andrews), Bethlehem, Bethnal Green, Bicton Heath, Birmingham Borough, Bootham Park –York, Bow (Somerset), Bracebridge (Lincoln), Brighton, Brookwood (Wandsworth), Burntwood, Camberwell (Clapham), Carlisle, Colney Hatch, Coppice (Nottingham), Coton Hill, Dartford (London), Fort Pitt, Glasgow, Grove Hall (Bow), Hanwell (Nottingham), Hatton (Warwick), Haydock Lodge (Merseyside), Hereford & Whitchurch, Higham Hall, Hull, Leeds, Mickleover (Derby), Morpeth, Northwood (Bristol), Norwich, Sneinton (Nottingham), Peckham (Surrey), Prestwich (Lancashire), Rainhill (Lancashire), Roxburgh, Salop & Montgommery, St Lukes (Liverpool), Stafford, Suffolk, Surrey & Three Counties (Stafford). For the Leicester Borough Asylum, which had opened in September 1869 there is considerable movement between its site & the County asylum. James a groom from Thrussington admitted in December 1849, was perhaps one of the most unfortunate mental patients of the Nineteenth Century as he was recorded: -

> 'Has been at various times in almost every asylum in the Kingdom and has broken nearly every bone in his body.' (186/1038)

The one other Asylum mentioned was the - The Royal Earlswood Asylum for Idiots in Redhill Surrey. After an unsuccessful start in 1848, in a building that was already standing, the asylum eventually opened in a newly constructed building in June 1855. It was the first establishment to cater specifically for individuals with learning difficulties. Patients slept in dormitories for fifteen & there was one member of staff for seven patients. John Langdon-Down, after whom Down syndrome was named, was a superintendent of the special asylum from 1855 to 1868. Patients had been taught various manual trades such as carpentry, printing, brush-making & also participated in domestic, garden & farm duties. Six of the Leicestershire County Asylum Patients had previously been educated there – Mantle (195/3763) from Barrow on Soar, Louisa (197/4437) from Ketton in Rutland, Frank (198/4899) from Enderby, John (200/5295) from Market Overton, Frank (200/5391) from Ratcliffe Culey and Gertrude (201/5413) from Woodhouse.

Two wards. Photograph courtesy of ROLLR.

Several patients actually chose to be a patient, with no virtually resistance to the admission process. Thomas (204/51) the pork butcher went to the relieving officer's house asking to be taken to the asylum, as he did not feel safe to himself or others. Ann a dissenting minister's wife was obviously ready for readmission too: -

> '...at her entrance in to the asylum she at once proceeded to take quarters in her accustomed place & seemed thankful for the protection which she felt would be afforded to her...is excitable at times but is generally cheerful and sometimes a little useful.' 187/1416 & 1468)

A framework knitter from Shepshed arrived at his local police station saying that he ought to be taken to the asylum (197/4593). Thomas (203/6178) a collier from Newbold who had also been a patient many times before, telegraphed the asylum in July 1900, two weeks before his admission saying "make ready". Mary Ann (210/108) a Griswold hand from Thurcaston, begged the doctors to protect her from herself as she believed that she was going to commit some horrendous act, which could well have been suicide.

One of the details required on admission was marital status. The position in the family did of course have a role within household relationships. Other halves had to cope with husbands being away at sea, husbands having been transported, husbands having deserted their wives. Husbands leaving wives frequently resulted in their partners being in need of the commonest necessaries of life. Eliza (187/1666) from Lutterworth's husband deserted her four days after the birth of her fourth child. Christopher (197/4511) a blacksmith's striker whose home address was in Worcester, but was working in Coalville, had not lived with his wife for two years and she had only seen him for 2 days during that period. Benjamin (205/112) was always quarrelling with his wife, but he did not desert her, one morning he ran her and his daughter out of the house. Isabella (192/2904) had to cope with exactly the opposite situation as her husband William had run away 9 years before & taken their 2 children with him. Hezekiah's daughter did not have to be run out of her home, she was so frightened of her father striking her again, that she left anyway (192/2930). A lady from Measham; -

> 'turned quite 'bitter against her husband & threw him down the stairs 3 weeks ago & threw things at him -She destroyed several things & had also done little housework & had also neglected to prepare food for her children.' (211/40)

A wife from Claybrook Magna: -

> 'Suddenly took against her husband - a poor harmless creature - whom she turned out of the house & threatened with a hot poker.' (211/150)

An Elizabeth (210/27) from Countesthorpe had threatened to cut her husbands throat, no wonder his contact address was given as Scarborough in the case book records. George (201/5542) who eventually became a patient himself was placed in gaol for a fortnight for the desertion of and refusal to maintain his wife & family. One of the most horrendous case book admission entries was that of Gertrude who had lived with her family near Sheffield and after being found to be chargeable to Barrow Union was brought into the County Asylum in December 1901, from Wadsley Asylum in Yorkshire. The newspaper cutting assumedly from a paper in Yorkshire, with the heading 'Scarcely Human', is still neatly adhered to her case book admission notes & has been there for 110 years: -

At Leeds Assizes on Tuesday before Justice Ridley, George Robert ….. was indicted
for the manslaughter of his daughter Gertrude Ellen May, and of his son, John Henry
at Sheffield and further with neglecting his children, thereby causing them unnecessary
suffering and injury to their health. After being prematurely confined the accused's wife
was removed to a lunatic asylum & the baby died. No less than four deaths occurred
within 17 days. The case investigated revealed horrible cruelty, the child being literally
starved to death. Inspector Stephens deposed that when he was summoned to the house
in November. Mrs ….. was dressed and 'staggering about the room' trying to attend to
her children. At the time the body of Willie was lying at the foot of the garret stairs, and
was becoming offensive. Nothing had been done to prepare for the funeral. The judge:
The man is scarcely human it seems to me. It is the most shocking thing I ever heard of.
Had you spoken to him about it? The witness in continuation said that when he visited
the house on Nov 18th Mrs ….. was in bed with two black eyes - The prisoner was found
guilty and sentenced to 10 years penal servitude. Patient was taken to the workhouse
where she was very violent, excited, raving & foul language & was destructive Nov 25th
was removed thence to Wadsley Asylum (210/52)

It was not just the men who were at fault here, as an Elizabeth (187/1412) went to gaol for neglecting
her children and became insane through her remorse for doing so. Agnes from Oakham had suffered
physical abuse from her mother, whilst a child & was herself providing what she believed to be
justifiable punishment: -

'Says her mother hit her as a child, so now she hits her mother to correct her.' (212/2)

Martha (210/33) had apparently starved her children and believed her self to be the worst woman in
the world. There were some quite complex up and downs within relationships. Martha's story is quite
enlightening: -

'... what has been commonly called an ill assorted marriage, for her former husband
she entertained the fondest affection, for the latter unmitigated disgust , hence arose
those fruitful sources of domestic disquietude, unhappy comparisons, and mutual
recriminations, until the domestic hearth became desecrated and her home a hell upon
earth, how few of these instances are ever recorded, yet how fearfully, they add to the
long list of misfortunes and insanity.' (187/1347)

Elizabeth (193/3335) from Shepshed had had two children by her sister's husband. Clara (195/3943)
from Wigston was married to a man 'who was already encumbered with a wife' and who suddenly
absconded to America with her money. Mary (188/1833) had become very despondent due to,
'Some altercations with the person with whom she has been living in adulterous intercourse.' After
Rebecca's (200/5371) husband from Swannington deserted her she went to live with her former
illegitimate son. Charlotte (197/4409) from Hinckley had to cope with a husband who cohabited
with other women. Marianne (185/681) ended up with mania because her husband had wrongfully
accused her of infidelity. Phoebe (217/153) completely disowned all her family in Thornton. Not
everybody shared their homes with anybody and some future patients to the asylum were essential
virtual 'loners'. Robert (191/2701) from Knipton had barred and bolted himself in & refused all
communication with his neighbours and this made his friends solicitous for his safety. A female

framework knitter from Barrow on Soar was also recorded as, 'secluding herself from her usual associates.' (186/894) Mentally ill individuals were not just turned out of their homes they could be turned out of other establishments too. John a sawyer from Leeds had been turned out of a lodging house at 4.00 am on 21st August 1908 (the actual day of his admission) as: -

> 'His behaviour being strange - Said he was trying to catch pigeons which were carrying away on their backs the spirits of his wife & children.' (203/6183)

Individuals of all ages were admitted - the youngest were Arthur (195/3757) from Hugglescote and Cecil (204/23) from Market Harborough Workhouse who were both aged four, with the congenital handicap of 'idiocy'. The eldest to be admitted was a Mr Smith (194/3467) aged 99 years & slightly younger than him was Michael (199/5025) from Stathern who was 91. The following table shows approximate numbers within each age group from all admissions which must make allowances for the missing records or not known: -

Ages		Ages	
0-10	61	50-59	1029
19	294	60-69	791
20-29	1121	70-79	404
30-39	1328	80-89	94
40-49	1297	90-99	3

Incoming patients were also from all classes of society. There were those suffering from privations of the barest necessities of life and there were those who were from financially sound backgrounds. Frank a Congregationalist minister from Glen Parva, alleged cause of insanity, was the anxiety and clearing off the debt on a new chapel. He declared that he could only be admitted as a private patient & if he had a nice little single room he would be perfectly content to remain at the asylum forever. If patients had enough financial backing, then they could be transferred to private patient status. When money ran out then individuals would have to be moved to charity class. Generally speaking, if nothing else, the pauper lost their stigmatised identities as a pauper when they became asylum patients.

There was William (187/1404), who whilst in the workhouse was a refractory and troublesome pauper, but the Officer who conveyed him from the Union House to Leicester informed the Medical Officer on William's admission that as soon as he knew his destination he became tranquil and quite cheerful. Within an hour of his admission William was usefully employed.

As well as being defined by their age patients also usually had their specific religion recorded. Not all casebooks though had exactly the same page entry format. Some of the initial admission page sheets had the following three sections - character, education & religion all available for completion. From 29th June 1856 an individual's religion was noted but for approximately a quarter of all the entries, the religion was either not recorded or not known. Virtually one half of the known entries were either Church of England or Protestant with some being just 'church men' or 'church women'.

Almost twenty percent were non-conformist being Baptist (some specifically Ebenezer, Calvinistic, General or Particular), Congregationalists, Methodists (Primitive or Wesleyan) with Thomas (188/1808), William (188/1815) & Esther (191/2833) all being entered as 'ranters'. Fourteen incoming patients were recorded as being as 'salvationisits' or members of the Salvation Army[5].

There were 3 Plymouth Brethren and an Anne (199/5100) from Oakham was defined as a 'Plymouth Sister Brethren': there were also 3 Mormons or mormonites. Just over two percent were Catholic with Thomas (188/69) specifically being an 'Irish Roman Catholic'. It could be assumed that some of the patients were non-believers - Mary (203/6113) from Wigston may have been one of them for she refused to go to the chapel, or to have anything at all to do with the clergy. Elizabeth (188/1866) from Conduit Street in Leicester had not been in any place of worship for 7 years and William (191/2694) a framework knitter from Nottingham 'had no religion in particular'. There were some other less common or more specific religions: -

     Emil the groom was a Lutheran (204/74)
     Jacob the travelling jeweller was a Russian Jew (199/5124)
     William from Ullesthorpe was a Scotch Presbyterian (198/4882)
     Eliza was a Calvanistic dissenter from the Trinity Chapel (188/1742)
     Esther from Buckminster was an Episcopalian (189/2123)
     Frances from Loughborough was a free thinker (188/1951)
     James from Loughborough was a spiritualist (193/3330)
     John a collier from Moira was a reformer (191/2649)
     A lady from Marston Trussell was a high calvanist (190/2298)
     John of Loughborough a blacksmith was a member of the Latter Day Saints (186/968)

Of almost 335 imbeciles who became a patient 32% had no religion recorded, 52% were Church of England, 12% were non-conformist and there were five Roman Catholics & one Scotch Presbyterian. The figures for idiots recorded as having a religion are even lower. Out of 83 idiots within the number admitted to the asylum only 18% have a classified religion, 15% were Church of England, just 3% were Wesleyan Methodists and one young idiot John's (188/1851) religion was classified as an 'idiot'. Were the 'idiots' generally being credited as not having enough intelligence to be able to believe in or practise any form of religion? Many patients poor mental condition was almost certainly actually due to their religious beliefs. Certain patients believed that they had sinned unpardonable sins past any forgiveness, and that they could not put it right, however hard they tried, and were due to experience eternal damnation. John (217/301CCB) a medical student would have liked 'to fight Satan, but due to his poor physical state he doubted that he would be victorious.' Those experiencing the fear of their lost souls believed that they could never go to heaven and some experienced horrific dreams of going to hell.

Another important classification within the initial casebook record of each patient was the occupation that they had held before their admission, even though they were usually on admission very adrift from their former selves. Many records of previous jobs were blank. The highest numbers of admissions, where the prior profession was recorded, within certain occupational areas, would coincide with high numbers for those who were well enough to still be practising the

---

5   Asylum Case Books Records DE3533 (197/4533-197/4723-197/4752-198/4918-200/5223-210/10-210/93-211/61-- 201/5416-201/5594- 202/5870-204/44-206/35-218/311).

Asylum Chapel. Stewart Collection courtesy of ROLLR.

same occupations in the world outside the asylum walls. There were well over eight hundred from the service trades which included domestics, charwomen, laundresses, washerwomen, general servants, nurses, porters, cooks, housekeeper, footmen, game keepers, hotel porters, grooms, stablemen, butlers, gentleman's servants, ushers, page boys & those performing general household duties.

The other exceptionally high numbers noted were within the clothing trade, with almost seven hundred hosiery trade workers & also over a hundred & thirty working within the shoemaking trade. There were significant numbers of other craftsmen such as almost seventy tailors & drapers, almost eighty blacksmiths with framesmiths, almost eighty carpenters & joiners and almost eighty workers within brick making or bricklaying. It was not just those skilled with their hands who were affected by insanity, there were also the higher professions with veterinary men, surgeons, lawyers, solicitors, architects or draughtsmen, actors, musicians, chemists & druggists, artists, photographers, police officers, clergymen, physicians or surgeons, clerks or book keepers and almost fifty schoolmasters, schoolmistresses or governesses (including Sunday School teachers).

There were some quite unusual occupations too such as Charles (206/89) the 'aerated water manufacturer' (admitted July 1907), William (187/1514) an actual lunatic asylum attendant, Joseph (191/2797) a glass silverer (admitted January 1868), Elizabeth (185/845) a match seller & fortune teller admitted November 1847), John (197/4478) a Superintendent of the Fire Brigade from Ashby de la Zouch, Richard (197/4467) a blind town crier from Syston, Frederick (191/2627) a newspaper editor, Dennis (186/1188) a herbalist from Loughborough (admitted in June 1851), Henry (190/2438) a monk, Daniel (196/4229) a catholic priest from Quorndon, Hendon (206/87) a School attendance officer from Loughborough (admitted in July 1907) & Jacob (199/5124) a Russian travelling jeweller (admitted in November 1890).

Many incoming patients were unfortunately accredited with the occupation of being 'a wanderer.' Some of the wanderers were more acceptable in having unsettled residences as many were very genuinely seeking employment as William (187/1548) from Lutterworth had been. Loughborough Workhouse is even recorded in the asylum records as having a 'tramp ward' where James (200/5398) a railway labourer was admitted from in 1893. Joshua (206/125) was admitted from Narborough workhouse but had walked all the way to Lancashire. Admission to the asylum of these 'of no fixed abode' individuals at times involved the assistance of the police force. The police though were ultimately often the salvation for the mentally ill within their community. The constables had to deal with both their local residents & the wanderers who had strayed into their area. Michael (189/2035) a wanderer from Belfast had a monumental problem on arrival in England, as he could not speak a word of English, leading to extreme difficulties procuring food & lodging. He was eventually found wearing a few rags & biting or kicking anyone who approached him. William (205/137) from Wigston became a local-wanderer, for he had to be taken back home by the police, as he had completely forgotten where he lived.

It was a major problem, for the patients who had no relatives whatsoever, to verify their personal events before admission. As no friend or family member, including her husband, had ever visited Charlotte (197/4500) in the asylum they were ignorant of her medical history. She died three months after admission from a heart condition, probably acquired through previously having suffered from rheumatic fever. Bridget (201/5596) from Loughborough claimed she had been fraudulently admitted, but had nobody to back her up. Many with little or no supporting caring figure were brought in from a workhouse or as otherwise named 'the union'. The workhouses were usually interpreted by both insiders and outsiders as appalling places to live. Maria (212/39) was admitted to the asylum from Blaby Union suffering from dementia. In the column for recording when the 'Attack Commenced' the script quite clearly states 'since admission to workhouse.' The case notes record one quite tragic family group within Market Bosworth Workhouse: -

> 'Born in workhouse lived there all her life. Mother lives in workhouse & 3 other brothers
> & sisters. Mother feeble minded. Brothers, sisters imbeciles etc. all illegitimate.' (212/148)

The Commissioners for Lunacy could be scathing about workhouse care. They felt that there was absence of legal safeguards for patients, a lack of qualified staff, inadequate medical treatment, a prevalence of restraint, an improper diet, filth, a lack of space & amusements, and lack of proper patient records. The Lunacy Commission appeared quite content to leave the insane within workhouses if they were able to get on with the other workhouse residents. The Unions often took up a major part within the life patterns of Leicestershire's mentally ill or mentally handicapped.

What were otherwise quite supportive families often wanted to avoid the stigma of a relative as an asylum or workhouse inmate. It was almost always a whole family in a workhouse: It was almost always just one family member in an asylum. Committal therefore to the asylum did not involve committal of the entire family of the pauper, as regular admission to the workhouse might. Instead if the lunatic were the father, the remainder of the family was eligible for outdoor relief. It was frequently cheaper to keep a patient within a workhouse, than in the more expensive asylum. Thomas (185/665) a framework knitter from Leicester had been insane in Leicester Union for many years. He was just one of many incoming asylum patients who had been in a workhouse or various workhouses for quite prolonged periods. It was far more likely for the idiots and imbeciles who had come in as patients from the Unions; to have been there a considerable time. James (196/4152) & Robert (196/4146), both with congenital defects, had been in the workhouses of Lutterworth & Uppingham for over 20 years. Mary (195/3939) an idiot had been in Claypole Union Workhouse for over 40 years, the staff had found it exceedingly difficult to keep her inside, even in ice-cold weather. Charles (204/140) a framework knitter from Blaby had been in the workhouse for some months, as he was too old to work and had started to wander away and on three occasions search parties had to be sent out to look for him. Edward (196/4307) an imbecile from Billesdon, had spent all of his 49 years in a workhouse and he was recorded as 'having no one who belongs to him'.[6] Emily (196/4265) a ten-year-old imbecile was brought in via Market Bosworth Union, but was essentially a <u>foundling</u> and having no records, tragically came from nobody or nowhere. She was a very well behaved and quiet little girl, who became a great favourite in the Asylum. Needham (187/1348) from Leicester Union, also had absolutely no connecting links, as there was absolutely no means of ascertaining his parentage. It is possible that some of those imbeciles or idiots, most with congenital defects, were virtually rejected at birth or soon afterwards. Helen (210/143) who was admitted in 1903 as a transfer from an imbecile institution in Birmingham, because she was so unmanageable there, had no known relatives to the asylum staff, but she was transferred to Private Class by her own solicitor, who perhaps was more aware of her parentage?

Patients of all ages, sexes, religions, and occupations and from various locations such as their own households, prisons or workhouses therefore came to be admitted as patients. Every incoming patient was subject to a detailed examination by one of the asylum's Medical Officers. On arrival at the 'House of Cure' the doctor would usually first give a brief synopsis of the basic visual appearance of the future patient. One officer at the time of admission was quite annoyed about the admission of William an intemperate framework knitter: -

'This case is a very deplorable one he seems to be sent into the asylum simply because he is dirty and troublesome.' (193/3373)

Ann (186/1060) admitted in March 1850, as an idiot from Kegworth was in quite a state by time of her admission: -

'The external appearance of this patient on admission was extremely unfavourable, being most slovenly in her person, and dress covered in vermin, having her head and various parts of her body severely burnt and in a wretched debilitated state of health ...she has been farmed out amongst her friends by whom she has been cruelly neglected, there is also great dereliction of duty on the part of the Parochial authorities in allowing such a case to be kept, for so long a period, out of hospital where by judicious treatment in the early stage of her malady much benefit might have been conferred , as it is, there is but too much reason to fear that she labours under disease of the brain, and is consequently hopelessly and incurably insane ...the patients fits were of the most severe character and she was seldom free from them, the exhaustion they occasioned at length wore her out, and it appears she was the last of ten children all of whom as well as the mother died from the same cause.'

There was Elizabeth (186/1097) from Shepshed: -

---

6   Leicestershire & Rutland Lunatic Asylum Case Books DE3533-196-4307

'Certainly a more wretched object never entered the walls of a Hospital. She is literally nothing but skin and bone.'

One wonders what condition the elderly widowed Elizabeth from North Ranceby in Lincolnshire (admitted from Sleaford Union in August 1846) must have been on entry, as there were instructions for staff to shave & well cleanse her head. (185/714) Then there was Henry (186/903) a 23 year old watchmaker admitted in October 1848: -

> '... he fancied he had committed some heinous offence against the laws of the country, for which he was about to be brought for trial with many other vague and enormous notions, his intellectual faculties are nearly obliterated and his understanding a sad wreck - it is truly lamentable to behold one so young and who only a short time ago gave promise of great usefulness, suddenly prostrated by the worst of all ills that flesh is heir to - he was literally nothing but skin and bone, by constant perseverance, however, in the administration of sustenance both by feeding and injection, he at length showed symptoms of improvement and rapidly recovered.'

The elderly John (185/720) was really empathically described by one of the medical officers: -

> 'His general conduct characterised by the greatest decorum, his disposition was gentle kind and amiable - he was always dirty in his habits more from the effects of disease peculiar to his advanced life, than from the natural in attendance to the dictates of nature...

There were many like John who was desperately in need of a bath at the time of admission. Giving patients a much-needed bath could be full of deep-seated problems. Firstly, staff shortages could arise if several members of a team were taken up with just one highly, uncooperative patient and a bathtub. A bath needed water & the local waterworks company was unfortunately at times exceptionally unreliable in either providing enough of it, or in providing water of a reasonable quality. The supply was noted several times as being of a very interrupted character and the Superintendent had to make arrangements for the asylum's own well to be used. In December 1893 the official visitors had seen the analysis of the water from the Asylum's own well and regretted that it was entirely unfit for drinking purposes. The water used for baths, the laundry & in the kitchen was needed to be hot. When William (186/1301) a printer was ordered a hot bath the actual temperature being recorded as '96 degrees Fahrenheit' in November 1852. The Asylum Superintendent seemed at times to be having more problems with the asylum heating requirements than the patients themselves. There were frequent journal entries relating to innumerable problems with boilers & pumps, chimneys, engines & pipes. If it was not a problem with boiler then it was difficulties with the actual coal supplies to run it.

> 9th March 1892 In view of the imminent coal strike & of others that may succeed in the future, it is respectfully suggested that as soon as may be conveniently carried out, a stock of coal be laid up on the Asylum grounds say 100 tons, so as to obviate the terrible straits the Institution would be thrown into in case at any time the contractor should be unable to draw the daily supply. We live now as regards the supply of coal from hand to mouth and often have less than a ton in the Coal Yard.[7]

---

7   Superintendents Journal DE3533-88 Journal IV

Fortunately, the majority of patients arrived at the asylum in a reasonably clean condition. Elizabeth from Earl Shilton was credited with both favourable appearance and good behaviour on admission: -

> 'The external appearance of this patient on admission was very favourable, being extremely neat and respectable in her dress, clean in her person, tolerably tranquil in her mind, and apparently in good health…neglected her usual occupation and enjoyed the luxury of silent thought.' (186/1026)

Indeed a very strategic part of an incoming individual's possessions were the actual clothes on their backs. Some patients of both sexes were very particular about their appearance. Mary (195/3801) who arrived from Willoughby Waterlees was probably one of the fussiest dressers: -

> '… dresses extravagantly she had on 4 shawls, 4 petticoats, 3 poultices and a quantity of farthings, & small coins among much rubbish in her pockets, & was swathed in a blanket.'

Ann (196/4136) from Ashwell (Oakham), was decked out with ribbons and odd bits of coloured finery. Maria (196/4305) from Belgrave was dressed in her own clothes and looked quite magnificent as she had dyed her hair, pencilled her eyebrows and was quoted as 'over disfiguring herself with makeup'. This same Maria was very much ashamed of having become a patient in the asylum & hoped that nobody knew that she was there. Hannah (192/3063) from Long Clawson was 'apt to arrange her hair in fantastic fashions'. It was not just the female new arrivals that were flashy dressers. Thomas (204/88) from Nuneaton 'brushed his hair & curled his moustache in a most scrupulous manner'. Philip (205P8) an artist by profession 'would decorate himself with flowers & feathers'. Joseph (206/111) a framework knitter from Packington Hill, Kegworth also had a tendency to grotesqueness of dress and would frequently have a sprig of boxwood in his buttonhole. John (203/6062) a labourer from Sharnford must have been very confident about his good looks, as at the time of his admission he handed the doctor a postcard of an actress & informed him that it was a picture of his wife.

A detailed medical examination was also made of each patient on admission. The following are three examples taken from the Case Books: -

> 'Lionel (193/3162) is a man of average height with well-proportioned and well-nourished frame: tolerably well formed head and good features with dark eyes and hair, the pupils are slightly dilated. The tongue is furred and the bowels obstinately costive the pulse is regular the viscera appear healthy. The veins of the upper legs are varicose apparently from sluggish action of the liver. The hepatic dullness is somewhat larger than natural there is however no tenderness over this region.'

> 'Emma (193/3131) is a tall and well-proportioned woman with tolerably nourished frame, well-formed head and pleasing expression of countenance. She has sandy hair and grey eyes with somewhat dilated pupils. The tongue is furred and bowels costive the pulse variable but usually of fair strength. There is a little uteric discharge and the breasts are full.'

> 'John (193/3092) is a tall man with thin & badly nourished frame, greyish hair and light grey eyes. There is a large depressed fracture of the right parietal bone of old standing.

There is talipes varus of left foot said to result from old injury to the ankle, and he is
much paralysed on the left side he appears in very feeble health. '

One of the most commonly used terms within the framework of the casebook records was 'hereditary'
or 'heredity'. Making the usual allowances for missing data there are approximately just over one
thousand admissions are recorded as having another family member with mental health problems. Just
fewer than two hundred incoming patients have more than one relative with a history of mental illness
& just other forty patients have three or more family members affected. Two patients are recorded
as having 'many' relatives mentally afflicted & twenty patients have the term 'several' used within
the hereditary classification column. The sister of Sarah (212/94) from Leicester stated that, 'All her
relations on her mother's side are very sensitive'. Hereditary aspects are recorded for each & every
patient including those with mental handicap. Ten idiots & one hundred & two imbeciles are recorded
as having relatives with mental illness or handicap. Elizabeth from Kirby Muxloe an idiot arrives in
January 1862 her brother Henry also an idiot comes in to join her in April 1865, both arriving at the
age of eight. Alfred from Narborough has a brother Joseph who is also an imbecile. Various family
relatives are linked to the 'idiot' admissions but only one is clearly stated to have an imbecile brother
where the rest may not be mentally handicapped but mentally ill. Virtually a third of the three hundred
imbecilic patients were noted as having mothers, fathers, brothers, sisters, grandparents, aunts, uncles
or cousins with mental difficulties. In the cases where incoming patients were illegitimate, details of
other family members suffering from mental illness would be incomplete as was the case for Annie
from Loughborough Union (212/38). The medics appeared far more confident in their diagnosis of
mental insanity if there was knowledge of another family member being likewise afflicted.

The following table shows the numbers of specific close relatives which were actually recorded within
the case books to also have suffered from poor mental health: -

Father	128	Son	15
Mother	142	Daughter	11
Brother	142	Uncle	87
Sister	155	Aunt	64
Grandfather	23	Cousin	58
Grandmother	28	Great aunt	5
Great Uncle	3	Niece	15
Nephew	7	Granddaughter	2

Philip (206/131) from Ashwell near Oakham probably had the most tragic family history. His mother
had cut her throat and his brother & sister had both drowned, (it is not clear whether the siblings had
committed suicidal acts). For some the words 'in a low way' are used to describe other family members
who even though they have no history of insanity, they have been or are very far from their best.
Classifying the newly admitted with an instant name for their mental distress was often a formidable
task for the asylum doctors. The only help the asylum medical men would usually get for some patients,
often came from the correspondence from various local doctors or regional officers who had come to
the decision for the need to admit local mentally ill individuals, or those discovered within their area.

The principal terms used within any diagnosis were dementia, mania, melancholia or congenital idiocy and imbecility. These basic mental conditions were frequently more specifically descriptive when coupled with adjectives such as acute, sub-acute, chronic, confusional, congenital, convalescent, delusional, epileptic, impulsive, incipient, intermittent, moral, ordinary, primary, puerperal, recent, recurrent, religious, remittent, secondary, senile or simple. The strategic importance of an accurate classification of a patient's mental condition at the time of admission is emphasized by the following inclusion in the Medical Superintendents Journal 15th Sept 1869, with one of the phrases being actually underlined by the Superintendent: -

> "There has been considerable amount of excitement & confusion in the wards lately owing principally to the want of classification – and to the admission of some very maniacal patients."[8]

The following figures for admissions with certain forms of mental illness, must be viewed as very basic approximations as there are hundreds of readmissions, two blocks of one hundred and fifty two entries completely missing in 1895 & 1899, a sad lack of knowledge of some patients on entry, partially illegible entries, or various omissions and blank boxes which could infer that 'absolutely nothing' was better than wrongly classifying a patient. Over 60 years of admissions taken from 1845 to 1908 certain totals can be attempted. Those patients who are not recorded with any specific condition, over eight hundred of them, obviously hamper any accurate interpretation of the figures. The table on the following page does give figures for the brief diagnosis of the patient at the time of their admission: -

Condition	Female	Male	Total
Blank	415	405	820
Delirium tremors	3	17	20
Dementia	239	295	534
Hysteria	29	0	29
Idiocy & Imbecility	173	248	421
Insanity	11	12	23
Mania	1627	1445	3072
Melancholia	900	716	1616
Not insane	5	9	14

Roughly speaking there were just over three thousand patients with some form of mania, one & a half thousand with melancholia, just over five hundred with some type of dementia commonly senile, just over four hundred with congenital causes, just under 20 with insanity (and no more details), 20 with delirium tremors and 25 with hysteria in some form. Similar numbers of either sex suffered from various manias or melancholia. It just appears to be twenty-five women who were given the brief diagnosis of 'hysteria', hysteria having gained its name from the Greek word for 'womb'.

---

8   Superintendent's Journal DE3533-84

Fourteen new arrivals had a quite easily treatable, unusual condition for asylum admissions, which was 'not insane'[9]. The decisions of being 'not insane' were not immediately taken, as was the case for Henry (206/141) a licensed victualler from Syston who was a patient for the shortest period of three weeks, and he eventually left for the Isle of Man as quite 'an ordinary individual'. John (202/5848) a boilermaker originally from Lancashire was epileptic, but did not suffer from epileptic mania & was recorded as 'not insane' in June 1897. George (197/4609) formerly a draper's assistant from Barrowden, was released as 'not insane' after 10 weeks as 'Has not shewn any signs of insanity since his admission.' Annie (198/4980)from Belgrave was recorded: - 'I do not therefore consider her at this date to be insane or a proper subject for detention'. Samuel (190/2486) a plumber from Long Eaton appeared to have been admitted after a family quarrel about money and a lot of drinking, which probably led to his friends taking severe measures with him. He was discharged from the asylum at the end of 3 weeks. Patients eventually classed as 'not insane', stayed though within the walls for anything from 3 to 9 weeks, until the state of their sanity was accurately clarified. Sadly, only fourteen individuals were wrongfully admitted, whereas thousands of mainly, Leicestershire residents were tragically very genuinely mentally ill or mentally handicapped and in desperate need of treatment within the County Lunatic Asylum.

Photograph of 'Not Insane' Male Patient.
Asylum Casebooks courtesy of ROLLR.

9   Asylum Case Books Records DE3533 (196/4174), (196/4175), (196/4348), (197/4503), (197/4600), (197/4609), (198/4980), (201/5404), (201/5572), (201/5581), (202/5848), (202/5877), (206/103), (206/141), (211/138).

'She is a foundling. This little girl is very well behaved and quiet in the ward and a very great favourite with everybody.' (196/4625) Emily an imbecile from Market Bosworth Union admitted at the age of 10.

'His disease has been ascribed to his mother having been delivered by instruments at his birth.' (201/5535) Charles an imbecile from Uppingham

'His father & grandfather married first cousins His mother died here & his mother an imbecile like himself murdered his uncle' Thomas from Bitteswell admitted 17th January 1899 (201/5583)

'...there is every reason to suppose that if this patient had been placed earlier under proper medical treatment and not farmed out by the Union her mental state might have materially improved and her bodily condition too- the child is quick and intelligent and in the course of time, with the aid of a little instruction, may be taught to be useful to herself and others ..she is also subject to fits... there are also many vicious propensities and disgusting practices which have been allowed to spring up and gather strength and appear to have been perfectly unchecked and unrestrained.' Sarah an idiot from Harborough Union Workhouse (186/1181)

'He seems to have had no training in spite of his 10 years at Earlswood...Minnies all he sees and micks all he hears.' (195/3763) an idiot from Barrow on Soar

'The delicate state of this boy's health is such that he was placed in the female ward No 1 for a short period.' James a young imbecile from Earl Shilton (194/3686)

'He has been accustomed to live on bread solely; but beef tea has soon brought a colour into his milk white cheeks.' (Arthur an idiot from Hugglescote (195/3757))

Mental conditions leading to admission to the Leicestershire & Rutland Lunatic Asylum

There were many reasons why individuals eventually required admission to the Leicestershire & Rutland Lunatic Asylum. The youngest were the idiots (the profoundly retarded) & imbeciles (the severely retarded), generally caused by congenital defect, accident or infection: The eldest being admitted were those with major senile debilities.

Congenital Defects & Mental Handicap

There were those with a congenital defect within the County Asylum who were not technically 'insane' but were 'imbeciles' or 'idiots'. Two hundred & fifty three admissions are given the term congenital within the cause for their defect on their admission, but this did not necessarily mean that they had lower than average intelligence or inferior general life skills. Four incoming cases have their mental condition defined as 'congenital' but no further information is given. Two other incoming patients are recorded as being 'congenitally deficient'. The idiots & imbeciles had to be assessed on admission and subsequently during their time as an asylum patient. The medical officers usually attempted to assess their basic abilities – Could they do simple addition sums? How many pennies there were in a shilling? A woman from Orton on the Hill named Mary (186/944) is recorded - 'she has neither memory, understanding, nor even the power of comparison'. An imbecile from Kibworth Harcourt's certificate on admission read, 'That he is quite a fatuous imbecile & has no mental capacity whatsoever.' Thomas did though have the mental powers to keep uttering 'Don't hurt me,' following his admission. (205/77) Naomi (210-107) from Coalville – 'had no intelligence beyond that she cried when she was hungry.' Did they know the names of common objects or the days of the week?

> 'Not withstanding his advanced stage of idiocy the patient has some slight degree of intelligence such as coming when called & recognising persons whom he has several times seen - He seems very willing to do anything he is able & will lead helpless patients to the table at meal times.' James (192/2843)

From information given in the surviving casebooks from January 1845 until the asylum closure in February 1908, eighty-three admissions are classified as 'idiots' and 334 are recorded with the less severe defect of 'imbecile'. Sylvia from Melton admitted in 1884 as an imbecile is recorded as: -

> 'Has been idiotic since birth - Eyes are completely useless as organs of vision -Has no idea where she is having some fixed idea that she is at Ratcliffe College -Talks to herself carrying on a continuous conversation of questions and answers - Frequently hums tunes to herself on being asked the name of one laughed and said "The Body Snatcher's Waltz Mr William"' (197/4454)

This entry exemplifies what was often a complete lack of clarity between these two types of mental handicap and "the village idiot" was frequently just "the village imbecile". William an idiot from Burrough admitted with mania really appeared to suffer within his neighbourhood: -

'...and this deviation of ordinary behaviour has been a source of great disquietude and personal inconvenience, he has for one and thirty years past been the idiot of his village, the laughing stock, and the butt of all unthinking and inconsiderate persons during nearly the whole of this time he has gone very scantily attired without any covering on his head, unshaven and unshorn? and it was only when the Magistrates of the district threatened to interfere in his behalf that his friends beside themselves and placed him in a proper asylum.' (186/1071)

At times patients such as Esther (210/42) were described as being 'simple minded'. Mary Ann from Barrow on Soar Union was admitted with mania but the notes stated: -

'Patient has always been weak intellect & classed as an imbecile for the last fortnight.' (212/33)

Elizabeth (212/116) from Enderby was admitted as an imbecile with melancholia & the Relieving Officer had written, 'Never was quite the same as "other girls". Another woman (190/2501) from Woodhouse Eaves unfortunately had several relatives who were 'imbeciles & almost idiotic'. Many of the admissions were admitted under the classification of 'imbecile' but were continually in the successive case notes referred to as 'idiots'. Was Thomas (205/77) of Kibworth Harcourt an imbecile or an idiot, " a fatuous imbecile & has no mental capacity whatsoever?" There are perhaps a few cases where individuals appear to have become imbeciles outside of their childhood years. As at times the term 'imbecile' seems to have been injudiciously given? Mary an imbecile from Deal was an excellent musician and played the piano much to the delight of the other patients. Daniel (189/2144) an 'imbecile' had been a policeman, a porter, a grocer or a tobacconist and in this latter capacity he had embezzled some property entrusted to his care.

Several of the admissions classified as 'idiots' or 'imbeciles' were exceptionally young in comparison to the general age of the clientele within the asylum. The following are all the admissions under ten years of age – Cecil from Market Harborough Union & Arthur from Hugglescote were aged just 4. John from Thorpe Satchville, Edith from Knighton, Mary from Burton Overy, Horace from Nether Broughton & John & Willie from Melton Mowbray were all aged five. Thomas from Ellistown & William from Redmile were both six. William from Shepshed. Mary from East Morton, Walter from Swinford & Frederick from Knighton were all aged 7. Henry & Elizabeth from Kirby Muxloe, William from Castle Donnington & Alpheus from Wymeswold were all 8. Arthur from Harborough Union, Sarah from Leicester, James from Earl Shilton, Edward from Ashby de la Zouch & Maria from Loughborough were all 9 years of age. Fifty-three admissions were aged 12 or under. There were though also 'idiots' & 'imbeciles' of all ages.

Age at the time of admission	No of patients admitted as idiots	No of patients admitted as imbeciles
10 & Under	18	17
11 to 16	17	38
17 to 21	12	63
22 to 30	15	74
31 to 40	6	55
41 to 50	4	46
51 to 60	4	24
61 to 70	0	7
71 to 80	0	3

Elizabeth (186/1053) was recorded as the supposed cause of her complaint being 'natural imbecility'. Four elderly patients are noted to be suffering from 'senile imbecility'. The eldest idiot was James aged 60 whom even though he is listed, as a having a brother Stephen, was always a pauper of no fixed abode. He died at the age of 66 in the asylum. Harriett (194/3715) from Witherley is admitted at 50 years of age & dies aged 67. John (192/3045) from Shepshed was the eldest recorded imbecile, on admission, at the age of 73 & was found totally restrained for his safety before admission. Seven of those classified as imbeciles, three men & four women, were actually recorded as married. All of them had mothered or fathered children – Elizabeth (194/3541) from Moira had 6 children, James (190/2370) & Jemima (189/1993) both had 4, Frederick (196/4252) had 3, Daniel (189/2144) had 2. Nine female imbeciles had just one child[10]. There is one idiot, Mary (195/3746) from Breedon on the Hill who is also recorded as having a child. Jemima's (189/1993) husband George had left her to probably cope on her own.

The younger idiots & imbeciles were often one amongst a family. Charles (201/5519) was an imbecile & was one of seventeen children: Mary Ann (211/90) from Overseal was an idiot & was one of sixteen. Sometimes congenital defects ran within families & taking one example Herbert (200/5258) from Eastwell had two idiot brothers within the asylum and a family from Peatling Parva had eight immediate family members with mental defects. For Elizabeth (200/5224) from Lutterworth both her mother and brother were imbeciles. Elizabeth from Woodhouse Eaves case book record states,

> 'This is case of mental imbecility of some degree this patient has been a well-known village idiot for many years…several of her relatives have been imbeciles & almost idiotic.' (190/2501)

Henry (191/2588) from Kirby Muxloe had a sister in the asylum with him & a brother with the same congenital condition, in a non-recorded location. Alfred (206/130) from Narborough was classified as an idiot, his brother Joseph (204/6) also a patient in the asylum was recorded as being an

---

10   Asylum Case Books Records DE3533 (189/2161), (190/2507), (194/3486), (195/3753) (197/4412), (199/5057), (200/5350), (201/5583) & (202/5851).

imbecile. The idiot & imbecile patients could be expected to have communication difficulties. A high percentage of the mentally retarded had little or no spoken language. Jane (194/3570) from Oadby could say nothing and some would utter just one or two basic words such as 'please' or 'Dada'. An imbecile from Woodhouse Eaves only knew a few words and those he knew he seemed to have been taught mechanically to repeat. (193/3267) Ada an imbecile from Thrussington is recorded as having spoken just one word: -

> 'It was noticed the other day that a trifle which irritated her she said "damn". This is the only distinct word that we have heard.' (199/5072)

Thomas (206/3) from Lyddington, one of the deaf and dumb mutes actually had some knowledge of the deaf and dumb alphabet.

Several of the mentally retarded patients had information in their records, which gave suspected reasons for their neural disability. Two of such admissions had added information on what may have caused the defect: -

> 'This is a case of congenital idiocy … she has never been able to utter any articulate sound…. She has no power of locomotion and is much deformed - mother fright of the waggoner being kicked by her door when pregnant exclaimed - God I am dying, the poor woman said she was never well after this occurrence. Ordered a circular belt and leather gloves a little mild aperient medicine a liberal diet and instead of being always fastened in a chair, which has hitherto been done by her friends, to be allowed to roll about on a bed upon the floor - nothing but education will avail in this case.' Emily (185/788)

> 'Mother had a fright during the third month of pregnancy'. Mabel (210/92)

The suspected cause of imbecility is also sometimes given with the casebook records. Francis (205/35) from Thringstone was up to 9 years old, like any other boy at school but after a severe attack of typhoid fever, he lost his sight, his hearing & speech eventually became inarticulate & for 15 years he had also been unable to walk. Walter (202/5878) from Swinford was a normal child going to infant school, until twelve months before his admission when he had a severe attack of measles, causing him to have epileptic fits. Frank (200/5391) from Ratcliffe Culey developed convulsions during his teething process. He sadly cried a good deal for his father, but was eventually released back home after two months. The cause of the imbecility affliction for Charles (201/5535) of Uppingham (born in 1877) & the more severe handicap of idiocy for Naomi (210/117) from Coalville (born in 1891), was that they had both been delivered by instruments at their birth. Harry (206/93) from Brighton had had an exceptionally bad fall at the age of two. There was also one evident case of some form of consanguineous relationships within a patient's family, as Thomas (201/5583) from Bitteswell, had a mother who was an imbecile but his father & grandfather had both married first cousins. Eliza's (195/3962) mother from Aylestone had had 14 children only 6 of them were living and they were mostly crippled or imperfect.

Most idiots & imbeciles were admitted from their own homes. Edward (205/110) from Oakham had quite a traumatic family history. He had been very weak minded since birth, his father was recorded as ill treating Edward's mother during pregnancy. He had been reasonably bright up to about 10 years of age but owing to his father's ill treatment of him he afterwards became ill both physically and mentally. He had had a private attendant for several years, but he was much neglected often being locked in a room for days. Admissions were frequently the result of a death within households. Elizabeth (210/106) from Market Bosworth, arrived at the asylum after spending three years in the local workhouse, where she had been taken immediately following her mother's death.

Looking after a close relative with exceedingly limited intelligence often put both parties in a position of danger. The 'simple minded' would get into fires, step into ponds or canals and there were threats to kill other children, rick burning and the hiding of sets of house keys to ensure that the police could not enter a house. Some could become violent & dangerous to others by lashing out with such things as furniture or household utensils. Arthur (202/5869) from Ashby broke almost all the teacups in his house. William (206/90) a young 11-year-old epileptic imbecile from Hinckley, had to be tied to a chair, otherwise he would rush out and get on the line at the nearby railway station. Another congenitally defective youngster ran into a railway wagon & fractured his clavicle in 1882 (196/4323). Edith aged five from Knighton caused quite severe problems within her own household.

> 'She is very troublesome at home - throws things into the fire and is destructive, she knocks the other two children about, which are both under 3 years old - she does not exhibit the ordinary & natural curiosity of a sane child.' (199/5027)

Henry (198/4901) from Ashby Magna the fourteen-year-old son of a farmer, who is described by the asylum doctor 'as a feeble young idiot' was the subject of much interest in a town newspaper. He was at a Leicester Court charged with attempting to murder his mother. He had greatly annoyed his sister who complained to his mother. The boy then attempted to secure a gun to shoot his sister but he was prevented in this and was punished by his mother. He then seized a knife and deliberately stabbed his mother in the side, inflicting a dangerous wound. The mother lost a great deal of blood and her life was at one time in great danger. Evidence was given showing the lad was of weak intellect and he was ordered to be removed to the Lunatic Asylum November 21st 1898. The asylum doctor found it hard to credit Henry with intelligence enough, to perform the designs and actions, recorded in the newspaper article.

Several of the imbeciles had to be admitted due to their absolutely unacceptable sexual behaviours within their families or communities, such as exposing themselves to members of the opposite sex. Harriett (210/121) an imbecile from Broughton Astley, had been exposing herself in the local streets. Indecently assaulting members of the opposite sex was a far more serious act within families or the local communities. Herbert (206/59) from Bardon had tried to interfere with his younger sister on the day of his admission. It is evident from the case notes that 'normal' males could wrongly take sexual advantage of weaker minded females in a community. Esther (210/42) from Earl Shilton was married with 4 children, but was described by the Relieving Officer as, 'a simple minded girl who ought never to have got married'. One imbecile (193/3370) was actually delivered of a baby whilst an Asylum patient. Behavioural difficulties sometimes though had their origins from completely the opposite way round, for Caroline from Ketton in Rutland was described on admission as follows: -

> '... the patients temper has been very irritable and her conduct extremely violent but both seem to have owed their origins much to domestic discomfort and to the brutality of her father who frequently beat this poor girl for a natural infirmity she could not always control ...' (186/1062)

Thomas from Hinckley was also given a dramatic description of parental damage on his admission: -

> 'He bears the unmistakable stamp in the face form & gait of having in all probability been begotten while the father was in a state of beastly drunkenness. '(194/3047)

Many idiots and imbeciles were successfully housed within the Union Workhouses until their behaviours became unmanageable. It appears from the case notes that Sarah Ann could have benefited from environments other than 'the Union': -

> '... there is every reason to suppose that if this patient had been placed earlier under proper medical treatment and not farmed out by the Union her mental state might have materially improved and her bodily condition too - the child is quick and intelligent and in the course of time, with the aid of a little instruction, may be taught to be useful to herself and others...she is also subject to fits... there are also many vicious propensities and disgusting practices which, have been allowed to spring up and gather strength and appear to have been perfectly unchecked and unrestrained'. (186/1181)

The use of restraints outside the asylum walls was one of the greatest concerns within the outside communities. The need for restraints was at times due to the delays in admission. John an imbecile from Shepshed, who in 1869, probably had the most elaborate form of restraints to protect him from hurting himself. He was recorded by one of the lunacy officers as follows: -

> ' ... seated on a strongly built chair the chair being fastened to wall with strong stanchions. John also had iron handcuffs on each wrist fastened together by a chain 10 to 20 inches in length. An iron anklet was lying near and staples were at the top and bottom of the chair. The connecting chain (of the handcuffs) was fastened to a staple in the windowsill so that the patient could stand up - altho' only in a constrained position. There was a staple and chair tied to the joining wall. There was an iron anklet fastened to his bedstead by a strong cord. An iron handcuff padded with rags & a strong leather strap was also lying near his bed.' (192/3045)

Many idiots or imbeciles were often tied with rope or chains to walls so that the family or immediate carers were able to maintain their occupations, which ensured that the funding was there for the next meal on the table & for essential clothing too. When William (195/4025) a 14-year-old idiot from Barrow upon Soar was found tied up with such a rope, in 1879, an order was given by 2 magistrates for his admission to the Asylum. Henrietta (195/3948) following a fall at 2½ years of age had always been an imbecile; after being found tied up to a wall in her home, as her mother was not otherwise able to work, she was ordered into the asylum as she was not under proper care & control. On admission, young John (206/10) from Redmile, had both hands tied in mittens. Clara (212/140) an imbecile from Great Bowden though sadly appeared to cause no difficulties, 'She sits down when told & there remains without any attempt to say or do anything.'

Incidence of epilepsy as a condition of an incoming patient

There are many records made of incoming patients also suffering from epilepsy. A high number of the mentally handicapped were recorded with this condition. There were 36 idiots & 91 imbeciles who were also epileptic. Many other asylum patients, who were not mentally retarded, also had to contend with 'fits'. Some patients were suffering from exceptionally severe forms of epilepsy. For Frederick (195/4074) from Grimston, 'The epileptic fits seem gradually to be wearing him to a shadow'; Sarah (192/2886) from Humberstone had such constant fits 'that her mind has been giving way in consequence.' Ann (197/4422) from Hoton is recorded as her 'intellectual powers appear to be becoming more and more blunted by her epilepsy'. At least 170 of the patient admissions were classified as suffering from 'epileptic mania'. Many an inmate of the Asylum had their insanity complicated by epilepsy, whereas the mental illness of others was directly accredited to it. Epilepsy was not always a pre-diagnosed condition there were occasions when fits were noted during the treatment period within the asylum. Several of the inmates on admission had evidence of a hereditary preconditioning to the disease. William (187/1420) a framework knitter from Enderby had five brothers & a sister - 'who have likewise been subject to the dreadful disease'. At times epilepsy was queried on asylum entry but Eli (196/4244) an imbecile from Halstead, soon showed his propensity to this affliction, by experiencing 3 major fits, during the first 12 hours of his admission. Epilepsy was not always linked to mania with the aforementioned John (202/5848) an epileptic from Lancashire being discharged after 6 weeks as 'not insane' in June 1897.

The epileptics admitted to the Asylum had suffered from epilepsy from quite different times in their lives. William (187/1716) a baker had had fits since birth, Sarah Elizabeth (192/3052) from 8 months, Thomas (195/4037) since 2 years old & Ann (191/2718) since she was 14. Many of the inmates had become epileptic in their later lives due to certain specific events. Most of the happenings were some form of accident such as being kicked by or falling off a horse, wagons, chimney towers or ladders. George (200/5380) from Oakham whose father was a well-known jockey had had a serious fall from a pony whilst a child which, resulted in him having epileptic convulsions. A roadman from Sileby (204/82) had the cause of his epilepsy to have been due to a fall from a horse, resulting in him having been dragged along the ground, ten years previously. Fred (203/6170) from Loughborough had fallen from a girl's shoulder when he was an infant. George (193/3024) from Sapcote had been struck by lightning & Edward (197/4791) a soldier from Ashby de la Zouch had collapsed with sunstroke as a soldier on a march in Afghanistan. A railway train had frightened Elizabeth (192/2970) and Joseph (188/1779) a policeman, had had a brick thrown at him. A few residents had far more unusual reasons as a cause for the onset of their epilepsy. William (185/764) was suffering from epileptic mania of some years standing, as twelve years before his admission to the asylum he had been suddenly attacked by a man who had seized him by the throat and tried to strangle him. William's fits immediately supervened this attack. Another Walter (202/5878) from Swinford near Rugby was completely normal until a severe attack of measles. Eliza from Leicester had suffered trauma in her school days: -

> '... succeeded a fright she received in consequence of her schoolmistress having for some trivial fault, shut her up in a dark cupboard, her nervous system has never recovered the shock it received from that circumstance, and Epileptic Fits of a very severe character, and violent form immediately supervened upon the shock.' (3533/1173)

Elsie (201/5492) from Odstone also appeared to have the onset of epilepsy due to extreme fright: -

'Patient was said to be a bright child up to 7 years of age: then one evening one of her brother dressed himself up in a sheet and crawled around the room, this produced a great fright on her. Shortly afterwards epileptic fits showed themselves & have continued ever since, her mental condition has also gradually deteriorated and she has become quite beyond control at home.'

Martha's (186/1216) epileptic mania was felt to be due to the fright she had experienced from hearing music on Christmas Eve when she was only six years old. An event at sea whilst he was in the marines had a long-term effect on Thomas's health: -

'It is also complicated with epilepsy, the attack seems to have been brought on by fright at the time he was a marine and was occasioned by a storm at sea… He was four and a half year ago a marine his habits were sober and industrious.' (185/754)

Frances from Claybrooke also had quite an unusual reason suspected for epileptic onset: -

'She is said to have been of very active and temperate habits until the sight of much unalleviated misery in the West of Ireland in 1848 which produced a great depression of spirits which steadily increased epilepsy.' (187/1547)

Thomas from Seagrave's reason for the commencement of epilepsy is even more unusual as a primary diagnosis: -

'Three years ago the day before his marriage he had an epileptic fit - & a few days later had several more.' (204/124)

Epilepsy administered itself in varying forms. William (203/6071) a tailor from Loughborough was fortunate to just experience the less intensive petit mals, whereas, Alice (201/5459) from Seagrave had both petit and grand mals. Elizabeth (211/68) a 15 year old imbecile from Cosby was recorded as fortunately having 'not had fits since she had cut her teeth. 'Most with epileptic mania or other mental conditions with epilepsy too, had far more serious convulsions or seizures. Edwin (204/76) from Newbold Verdon used to define them as his 'sensations'. The timing and duration of the fits also varied much with every individual so afflicted. Some patients just had them at night whereas others had them both day and night. Several epileptics had the fits infrequently, but they could be severe and major convulsions when they did occur. Harriet (203/6091) from Leire traumatically had 134 fits within 2 days. Some had such a severe succession of fits that they went into 'status'. Letty from Ullesthorpe suffered from quite severe epileptic fits & eventually died at the asylum from 'status epilepticus'. The Relieving Officer had seen her having an attack prior to admission: -

'Previously I have attended her whilst she has had epileptic attacks & I have formed the opinion that in these attacks she is not responsible for her actions - was married 13 years ago & soon after began to have epileptic fits - which have become worse lately. Had has 8 children only 3 alive - had twins 4 years ago, dropped one down the WC which was suffocated - the other one died soon after.' (212/23)

Jesse (194/3618) from Humberstone would have long periods completely free from attacks, followed by epileptic status for 10 days in which he almost died. William (186/1000) from Earl Shilton lay for several days with scarcely any immunity from fits. The doctors would understandably frequently be called, if the patients were having major or a series of fits.

The incidence of epilepsy within an individual could cause major understandable complications when trying to earn a wage. Several had never had employment in consequence of their epilepsy. Many could only find flexibly timed temporary work as labourers to correspond with their fits. Some epileptics could be liable to be too excited & wild to be safe within certain fields of employment. Herbert (206/59) aged 15 had started at Bardon Hill quarries at the age of 13 after leaving school, but he had to give it up at the age of 15, when he started to have fits and from then on could only do simple jobs like tending cattle. Walter (205/42) another resident from Bardon Hill, 'was discharged from work on account of his fits, but declared he can 'gaffer' for himself. ' The more fortunate epileptics were those who could work within the trade of the family household, such as Henry (204/3) whose parents were drapers from Loughborough. Benjamin (204/60) from Ashby de la Zouch, who was hardly ever free from the effect of fits, lived with his father and was employed as a farm labourer at odd jobs, 'but could not be trusted far'. William (205/91) from Market Harborough had quite a tragic career history. He started for 3 or 4 years as a railway porter, but was discharged when 19 years old on account of his epileptic fits. Following this he was employed to carry a letter bag, but due to him having a fit, causing the seal on the bag to be broken, he had to give up the job. He also had to contend with being nicknamed "Silly Willy" within the district where he lived.

Many of those patients who were epileptic had in consequence quite variable temporary derangements. For many the state of mind before or after a fit could be just as problematical as the fit itself. Alfred (187/1645) a brush maker would after a succession of fits, attempt to get out of a window. Frank (204/130) from near Rugby would kick and roll about the house after his fits. Patients who were normally quite calm & friendly could become in contrast quite abusive and violent. Harriett (203/6091) from Leire often threw the food and the vessel containing it at her nurse. The Medical Journals have entries where an epileptic patient had to be placed in seclusion for a couple of hours due to 'epileptic excitement'.

Special safety precautions had to be taken within the asylum for epileptics. They would often share a specially selected Asylum ward with the potentially suicidal patients, as both needed to be carefully observed. At times other patients were very aware of those suffering from epilepsy and Charles (195/3900) a butcher from Moira was ready one day to give a fellow patient a drink of water after an epileptic episode. An epileptic from (193/3339) Enderby was recorded as 'falling like a log, usually on his face, resulting in frightful wounds & bruises. A fancy worker from Mill Lane in Leicester, had broken both her arms & right leg because of falls from fits. (192/2895) Hannah (210/64) from Loughborough, had 15 months before her admission, fallen in a fit into the fire & burned her face so badly she had had been a long term patient within Loughborough Hospital (her photograph at the time of admission emphasizes the extent of her facial disfigurement). Some had such violent fits at night that they had to have their mattresses on the floor to protect them from injury. William (185/881) from Leicester was also placed in a padded room with a bed on the floor, for his better security. Suffocation was the due cause of death for four epileptics in the Asylum, due to entanglement with bedding or clothes.(188/1779-186/1017-196/4297-185/881) Patients did not need to be entrapped in fabric to lose their life. Catherine (186/1025) from Leicester suffered regularly from fits, frequently sinking from their violence, but she continued to rally from them, until the last series, when her fits so rapidly succeeded one another, that she died from exhaustion.

Epileptics would generally have the same opportunities as other patients when it came to how they spent their time in the asylum. Daniel (187/1491) a young epileptic from Mountsorrel was enabled to continue his apprenticeship as a shoemaker within the Asylum. Epileptic men would still travel to the asylum farm for what was often a therapeutic day, even if they had to be brought back, due to suffering a major epileptic episode. The farm they would be brought back from, at Newtown Unthank (near Desford) was about 7 miles away. The female epileptics would work in the wards, even if this had to be between severe epileptic attacks. Eliza (191/2810) a stitcher was one exception when it came to be free to enjoy any leisure activities in the late 1860's. Her fits though of short duration, were so sudden & severe, that she was obliged to be denied some little privileges, such as going to the Ball, Chapel & for walks. Young Fanny (200/5377) from Thurmaston South was perhaps more fortunate than the other epileptics – 'Has had a convulsion with screaming, but not like regular epileptic fit and according to nurses it looked as if she was "putting it on"'.

Photograph of a snow plough at the asylum.
Stewart Collection courtesy of ROLLR.

Generally speaking, the epileptics did not experience a great curtailment of activities during the day. William (200/5348) from Loughborough had 3 fits one day, the third occurring during a football match. George (195/4010) an epileptic assistant in the vegetable house from Garthorpe, was allowed beyond the grounds two or three times a week. Another George (199/5028) from Hugglescote had a convulsion one day whilst sitting on the grass watching some cricket & following the fit he was heard to say: -

    'Oh damn these fits.'

Approximately a third of the patients entering the asylum with epileptic symptoms died there from epilepsy, whereas a fifth recovered enough to be allowed home with no readmission recorded. For several their conditions were treated so successfully that the incidence of fits either diminished in frequency or decreased in intensity, such as John (185/672) a cellar man from Leire and Richard (189/2213) a carrier from Leicester. George (185/794) a labourer from Leicester was so well at the close of his stay that he replaced one of the regular gardeners and in doing so saved the institution finances considerably.

Early photograph of Fielding Johnson Building, c1922.
Photograph courtesy of University of Leicester Archives ULA/FG1/3/78 .

Problematical, dangerous or socially unacceptable behaviours before admission

It was for many their problematic behaviours that had almost directly led to their admission to the asylum. They did not have to be mentally retarded to cause very noticeable difficulties within their immediate environments. A hosiery seamer from Wigston Magna (197/4777) suffering from chronic mania was found cooking meat, sugar and tea together in frying pan. Mary Theresa (211/2) from Glenfield would go out gardening with a carving knife at 4.00 a.m. A married stocking maker (210/58) from Burbage had tried to rake out the fire with her hands. Matilda (212/60) was a concern to her family because she preferred to sleep on the hearth rather than in bed. If Fanny's (210/54) father from Knossington did not get her up & dress her, she would just stay in bed all day. A lady named Agnes from Long Whatton caused similar problems: -

'Has no volition, but refuses food, lies in bed like a log.' (212/37)

Certain patients had caused considerable difficulties within their own neighbourhoods. Sarah Ann (210/28) of Pinfold Gate Loughborough, collected old rubbish & put it through letter boxes. Another lady of the same name & place (210/29) was found one morning sitting on a neighbour's doorstep partially clad. Elizabeth from (211/4) Lutterworth walked about with a stick & struck out if she was contradicted. A servant named Maud (211/138) from Coleorton had threatened to set fire to a hayrick. Julia from Oakham, caused quite formidable problems in & around Oakham in 1907 by: -

'Stopping people when driving & asking for rides & directly she got in, she would not get out again.' (212/98)

Many individuals who had no evident immediate families also exhibited quite dangerous behaviours prior to admission. There were the wanderers who had ceased to be under any form of proper care and control. Edward (206/33) from Kettering was supposed to have possessed a wandering spirit & had been of the "knock order" all his life. Ruth (210/44) a shepherd's wife, from Eastwell near Melton Mowbray kept wandering from her house in her nightclothes & on one occasion was found near Belvoir Castle. Elizabeth (200/5250) was admitted on Christmas day to a workhouse, due to her wandering in extremely inclement weather conditions. She arrived at the asylum on 11th January 1892 and died from pneumonia there 6 days later. If a wanderer was going to wander from a workhouse, then they should not do so in the workhouse's own garments, because this would constitute a theft having taken place. Frederick (196/4252) an imbecile from Enderby, was one such wanderer & subsequently ended up in prison. William from Ashby de la Zouch was a somewhat excessive wanderer: -

'He is constantly pursuing some absurd chimera as - he will travel 20 to 30 miles a day on foot under the notion that he is compelled to do so and without any object.' (187/1327)

The drifters were usually admitted via police stations to the workhouse or the asylum. Robert (206/66) from Oakham Workhouse had never slept in a bed for many years and generally had just found a convenient out house. Thomas (192/3075) from Loughborough who was found lying in the road drunk by the police, having an epileptic fit, was even more likely to end up as an asylum admission. A wanderer exhibiting strange behaviours was almost inevitably admitted, as was the case of Charles (204/22) from Blaby who was found hugging a tree under the impression that he was saving a lady from drowning. Wandering was at times linked to some degree to intemperance. One patient (205/29) is recorded as having been admitted from Leicester Prison Infirmary Ward after having been certified insane for attempting to cut his throat.

Several others were criminals within their own households. Neil (205/15) of Thurlaston, had attacked his father with an axe and thrown pots at his mother. John (186/1048) of Swinford entertained the greatest dislike to his relatives, several of whom he has attempted to injure, he struck his brother a violent blow on the arm with a stick, trampled on his father's toes and nearly succeeded in throwing his sister over a high staircase. An engine driver from Pinfold Gate in Loughborough (194/3612) was recorded as 'kicking his little daughter around the kitchen.' Asylum patients were also noted for making murderous attempts on their next of kin. Violent behaviour was not only a problem within the immediate household at times, it would be a problem for individuals who were totally unrelated to their mentally ill assailants, as was the case of Albert a clerk from Glenfield whose actions were recorded in a local newspaper in October 1903: -

> '…extraordinary occurrence at Kirby Muxloe Doctor Attacked by Lunatic. The moment Dr Garfitt appeared at the door … sprang at him, seized him by the throat, and dragged him out into the garden shouting excitedly that he meant to kill him, and behaving generally like a mad man. Taken unawares the doctor had at the outset, the worst of matters in the terrific struggle, which ensued. There were unfortunately, only ladies in the house, and they were too frightened to render any assistance, but one had sufficient presence of mind to send a servant to the residence of a gentleman living a short distance away, and he at once went to Dr Garfitt's aid. By this time however, the doctor had gained the mastery over his assailant, whom he held to the ground pending the arrival of a constable. The madman for such he undoubtedly was, who had almost exhausted himself by his violent but fruitless struggles, was secured by means of a cord, and conveyed to the county police station at Leicester. Here he was handed over to the care of Supt Ormiston who by kindly treatment succeeded in quieting him.' (205/13)

Marianne (186/1023) from Leicester struggling with her husband's suicide, as a patient herself, had before admission threatened to destroy her children. Annie (212/44) from Atherstone actually threw her children out of doors. One mother (211/80) from Markfield, came to believe that her eldest child was not her own, but had been introduced into the house in the middle of the night. A Mr Lord (189/1029) from Hinckley was problematical in a completely different way, as he actually begged his relatives to send him to the asylum. John (199/5062) a rat catcher was shown to be exceptionally dangerous as 15 years before his admission he had threatened his wife with a revolver filled with nails and slugs, his wife had managed to knock the pistol down and the charge consequently entered his right leg, which afterwards had to be amputated. Elizabeth (191/2828) from Newbold Verdon was greatly annoyed by local children owing to her eccentric ways and she ran with an open knife after a neighbour's child who had teased her. It was decided that Sarah (210/21) should be admitted quickly in March 1901, (whose length of attack, had only lasted one day), 'as she might go and jump in the river which was just opposite her house in Quorndon.' Mary Ann (210/12) from Medbourne was admitted after she suddenly bolted from her house & ran up the nearby railway in her socks, for over a mile. Both Susan (210/69) from Oadby & Mary Ann (210/126) from Syston placed lighted candles on beds & by doing so nearly set their homes on fire. An aunt of an Elizabeth (211/44) from

Quorndon had hot cinders thrown all over her. Another family and community problem were family members going outdoors quite inappropriately dressed. Frank (205/88) from Thorpe Langton was appropriately dressed but he initiated an enormous horticultural disaster. He heaped together in a trench the entire seeds of his brother a gardener.

Certain patients were actually recorded as criminals on admission. The crimes that they had committed were various – going out begging, systematically stealing working implements, potatoes, books or portable articles, picking pockets, absconding with a horse and trap, poaching, placing obstructions on the railway, indecently assaulting females and breaking into houses. They were several quite interesting criminal patients. A collier from Coalville (195/3754) is actually recorded as being a 'kleptomaniac'. Thomas (204/88) an imbecile from Nuneaton was declared 'unfit to plead' in 1901. Henry (205/130) was discovered by the police in Melton wandering about & pulling up vegetables in an allotment garden. A sixteen year old lad from Birkenhead was an unusual admission: -

> 'This lad was sentenced on Dec 22nd 1888 at Hinckley to pay £2.06 or 21 days imprisonment for travelling on the Railway without a ticket. He says he was a stow away on board a vessel to New York. He considers himself as the personal friend of the Tsar and the President of the United States.' (218CCB/309)

Richard (197/4467) the town crier from Syston, had been virtually blind since childhood only being just able to discern where the fire in the asylum was. He unfortunately had picked up the practise of going out & sawing down other people's railings for firewood. Catherine (194/3433) a mother from Countesthorpe was admitted from the County Prison for, after fearing her daughter would be induced into an immoral life, had cut her daughter's throat. Due to extreme anxiety following the death of her mother a lady from near Rugby had seemed to attempt to drown herself & her child in a pond. Following the death of the child in this event, the Coroner's Inquest returned a verdict of wilful murder and Mary (193/3154) was committed initially to gaol. Another distraught mother whose occupation was quoted as a 'tramp' had the following entry within the case books: -

> 'This patient was admitted into the Leicester Prison on March 5th 1890, charged with killing her youngest & 3rd child which was found buried in a field close to Loughborough and was awaiting trial at nest assizes.' (218CCB/325)

Catherine (202/5864) from Atherstone had unsuccessfully tried to force some 'revocide of mercury' into her daughter's mouth. Thomas (191/2760) a framework knitter from Stoke Golding, who became a patient, had been transported for life for murdering his criminally inclined brother-in-law. He was though so well behaved that he was allowed back to England. Marianne (186/985) from Willoughby Waterlees who was admitted through a Secretary of States Warrant had developed chronic mania soon after she was convicted for larceny & sentenced with seven years transportation. She was the mother of a large family and her husband had treated her disrespectfully by cohabiting with another woman 'this circumstance preyed upon her mind, and 'drove her off her head'. The same Marianne became exceptionally unwell when placed in a really damp cell. She eventually died of general paralysis after spending five years in the asylum. Mary (187/1380) from Barrow had as her root cause, her husband being transported away. Samuel (185/626) a labourer from St Margaret's on the other hand recovered in the asylum, but he had to remain in the asylum as a 'criminal inmate'. Tragically, Thomas (206/3) an imbecile from Lyddington had his usual residence on his death certificate still recorded in 1918 as a 'Police Station' because that had been his last address on admission to the Asylum 12 years previously.

Several patients had been previously assigned places in a workhouse to which they were directly chargeable. Joseph (197/4508) from Dunton Bassett was taken from raving at a racecourse to a workhouse. Eventually, the workhouse to where they had been allocated a place became no longer suited to their individuals needs. Paupers had become unruly, violent, and unmanageable with behaviours both extravagant & abominable. Alice a 40 year old from Uppingham Union, is recorded by her Relieving Officer as follows: -

> 'I have known her for several years as a quiet inoffensive mentally deficient inmate &
> have returned her quarterly as such - became troublesome in Union pulling old people
> out of bed.' (212/29)

Some had used threatening languages to the Masters or Mistresses. Fanny (210/48) from Uppingham Workhouse had disturbed inmates through her incessant talking & restlessness. Sarah (210/46) from Market Bosworth Workhouse 'had a vile temper.' Others were quite destructive breaking glass & furniture. Elizabeth (211/79) admitted from Leicester Infirmary Workhouse in November 1904, had dangerously wanted to walk about with a kettle of boiling water. One union inmate had made murderous attacks on other inmates & the cook. Martha (186/1194) from Ravenstone was defined as having very 'dangerous propensities'. Ann (191/2736) from Loughborough Union's 'conduct had latterly become outrageous'. James (205/123) an imbecile from Market Bosworth caused major problems by performing unnatural offences, such as practising sodomy with feeble-minded inmates. John (191/2755) from Ashby de la Zouch had tried to strangle other inmates. Some inmates had attempted to set the Union on fire. A couple had been troublesome at night-time by pulling off the bedclothes of others or by getting into their beds. Ann (211/120) admitted from Loughborough Workhouse: -

> 'Very troublesome at night empties the contents of the night commodes into the
> beds & drinks out of the pans, pulls the stuffing out of the couches & pulls the other
> patients about.'

The workhouse was for many a form of middle staging post between home and the asylum. Or the wanderer often went from a workhouse to asylum. James (206/148) was exceptionally noisy and continually had to be fetched for meal times. Samuel (195/4060) an imbecile from Loughborough also kept escaping from his workhouse and on one occasion threw himself into a canal. Sarah Ann (203/6126) from Nailstone related to the asylum staff how useful she had been in the workhouse - helping the nurses. In reality though it turned out that she was from all accounts a great nuisance in this respect, being constantly in the way and interfering. Eventually, many workhouses including Leicester had within the community a lunatic ward. It was perhaps within these separate workhouse wards that there were similar restraints to those used within the asylum. Jane (189/2233) from Oakham had been placed in a padded room in a workhouse. George's (191/2703) behaviour within Lutterworth Union Workhouse had become so outrageous that he had had to be placed in a strait waistcoat there. Many imbeciles or idiots were so therapeutically treated within the asylum's daily routine that their improved behaviours allowed them to be placed in a workhouse. For those who believe that workhouses used to be one of the last places any individual wanted to be on this planet - well Frederick (199/5903) from Oakham had been admitted from the Union, but he frequently told the asylum staff that he wanted to go back to the Union, 'to go home'.

Conditions suffered by female patients resulting in mental illness

There were mental conditions resulting in mental illness for just female patients. A few young women were admitted due to mental hardship at certain times of their sexual development in life. Jane (203/6203) was recorded as having problems with her adolescence; five other females were also noted of having difficulties with puberty and Mary (191/2835) a domestic servant aged just 14 was having difficulties with the 'time of life'. The ages of these girls or women ranged from 14 to 24. Following the teenage years there were lots of problems for women directly related to their gender. Sixteen female patients had 'menstrual irregularity', defective menstruation, supposed menstruation, amenorrhoea or obstructed menstruation as the reason for various mental conditions. There was also the case of Ann (186/928) where difficulty was experienced in controlling the fearful attacks of maniacal excitement, which occur at 'particular periods' (the particular periods was underlined). Was this a play on words with regard to the feminine experience? There was another female hormonal linked, later stage of life, which wreaked havoc with a stable mind. Sixty three women with ages between 36 and 60 years had the cause of malady claimed to be 'change of life', 'cessation of the menses', 'catamenia', or 'climacteric'. Sarah (203/6104) of Market Overton who had 8 children, was the one of three patients to be diagnosed of problems with 'the menopause' in December 1899. Elizabeth (211/54) from Loughborough in July 1904, 'Has lately suffered from insomnia - Menopause has come on'. Eliza (203/6065) was the only other patient with exactly the same diagnosis in May of that year. Half the women with 'change of life' type mental illness were cured; just about a quarter died and a quarter were long-term patients.

The most tragic time of life for many of the female admissions to the asylum was immediately following their children's birth. One hundred and fifty of the female admissions have the adjective 'puerperal' within their diagnosis. Fifty-nine cases mention pregnancy within the notes, without the adjective puerperal, but use such terms as parturition, pregnancy, childbirth, child bearing, result of confinement, lying in, demands of maternity. Sophia from Loughborough in 1870 had a blank cause for her supposed cause of malady but the case notes recorded: -

'The history given by those accompanying the patient is to the effect that she was about 5 weeks advanced in pregnancy when medicines were administered for the purpose of procuring abortion and that the mental disease closely followed one such attempt.' (193/3174)

There was Eliza the stocking maker from Leicester: -

'This patient has had 10 children very fast and the demands upon her system caused by maternity so frequently have been extremely depressing. She is in fact a mere animal vegetating from day to day.' (186/1140)

The admission of Mary from Derby also shows just how much women went through in maternity: -

'This is case of dementia the head affection came about 9 years ago after her sixteenth confinement at which time she had a severe attack of puerperal mania from milk fever.' (185/823)

The early loss of baby at times resulted in deep mental afflictions & not just overwhelming grief. A laundress from Hinckley (212/43) with two children had her supposed cause of onset as a miscarriage 3 months before. The reason for the childless Mary (185/857) from Rothley's admission, 'appears to have been the result of extreme debility occasioned by repeated miscarriages, which much reduced her.' Sarah (211/144) from Loughborough had a very premature baby that only lived a few minutes. Eliza (211/146) from Whitwick's baby only lived 5 weeks; the actual written cause of the onset of her mental condition was recorded as 'loss of child'. One of the most traumatic events of childbirth was surely to have been delivered of a stillborn baby. Sarah Ann (195/3888) of Normanton le Heath, Mary (191/2776) of Old Dalby, Emma (199/5031) of Loughborough & Sarah (201/5524) of Higham on the Hill all had the experience of a dead foetus. Hannah (210/96) from Loughborough had had to suffer the loss of 2 stillborn babies. The babies to whom a Mary (192/2906) and Eliza (192/2893) were confined both eventually died. Rebecca (187/1370) from Syston & her two months premature baby, both died the same day 7th July 1853 at the asylum. There is another tragic case of Eliza who was admitted with puerperal fever: -

> '....was seduced by a man who promised to marry her as the only way he could make up for the injury he had done her, when the time came however, for the performance of his promise he refused to perform it, and eventually deserted her, the shock to her feelings was so overpowering by this bitter disappointment, that she went raving mad and has continued so ever since.' (185/778)

In the number of children classification column of casebook records, Jane (199/5086) of Nottingham is recorded of having '9 children - buried 7'. In complete contrast to Jane, Catherine (203/6172) from Swannington was fortunate in having 10 children but did not appear to be possessed of any maternal affection for them. Hannah (210/17) from Castle Donington, suffering from both influenza & puerperal problems, had been delivered of her child just 10 days before her admission, and was recorded in the case book as saying – 'She thought that her baby sleeping inside her was dead'. For one case Mary from Long Whatton, was deeply troubled that she had been married for eleven years without becoming pregnant: -

> 'Goes to the police station & asks for a cup of tea, a few days ago went to the workhouse & says she was in labour. Goes to various doctors houses at all times of day & night for no apparent reason.' (210/24)

Thirteen females actually delivered a baby whilst a patient within the asylum. Only one of these patients was diagnosed with 'puerperal mania' all the rest of the women were suffering from mania (both chronic & simple), imbecility, hysteria or melancholia. Women were admitted in various stages of pregnancy and at times the mother's condition may not have been immediately apparent on admission. Sarah (197/4769) who arrived as a transfer from Nottingham Asylum, was though delivered of a baby an hour and forty minutes after her admission at the Leicestershire Asylum and Sarah Ann (210/23) from Rothley, was eight months 1 week pregnant at the time of her admission & her baby was delivered two days later. Mary (192/2954) a butler's wife from Goadby admitted as a patient after a horrendous labour took no interest in her child and would not nurse her. In 1882, Selina (196/4322) of Leicester was admitted with puerperal mania after having 'had an ordinary confinement and was downstairs about the usual time.' Looking after babies must have become just one more job for the already busy hospital staff. Mary (191/2785) from Mushroom Lane in Ashby had her perfectly formed baby very prematurely it weighed just 3 pounds 15 ounces – the baby weighed 6 pounds on discharge with its mother 6 weeks later. On 14th April 1875 two married women Rachel & Fanny who had been admitted whilst pregnant were both delivered of living children during that week: -

'These cases have been very disagreeable additions to the anxieties of Asylum life.'[11]

Baby's delivered live within the asylum had various futures. It seems that some stayed and were nursed by their mothers whilst others like Mary (200/5397) from Donington Le Heath's mother came to collect her grandson. Ann (193/3370) a farmer's daughter from Thornton suffering from imbecility, had her child adopted by relations of the asylum's head nurse. Sarah (195/3753) from Markfield was another imbecile who was also confined of a baby boy, just one month after admission but they went home together two months later. It is not always clear what happened to the babies of mothers admitted with puerperal type mania. Such is the case of Ann (190/2457) from Lockington, who did not manifest any affection for her child & believed it to be at Shardlow, but she had no idea who had actual charge of it. Mary (199/5099) from Freeby took absolutely no notice of her newborn child at all, she could only be kept in her house if the doors were locked & it is assumed that family or friends cared for the baby. Another Maria (192/2890) from Hinckley came in with her 11-week-old baby, but it was sent back to Hinckley after 18 days with its mother remaining in the asylum. Sarah (202/5803) from the Jolly Sailor's Yard, Hemington, admitted with puerperal mania, was very depressed & tearful wanting to go home to her baby. Mary Ann a shoe worker from Liverpool Street in Leicester was admitted following childbirth & the onset of puerperal mania: -

'…she had half a grain of morphia last night and slept well. 3/11/1868 Her child has been sent for, as it was very ill suffering from diarrhoea. It seems very emaciated. 10/5/1868 Mary Martin is quite rational and cheerful. She takes her food well and daily gets stronger. The baby is a great source of amusement to her. It is also improving in health.' (192/2933)

Esther (191/2833-193/3160) of Thurmaston bore two babies 33 months apart whilst a patient within the asylum on two separate admissions. For both these deliveries, there was a total absence of anything like labour and both times the baby just fell out, the first when she was standing in the passage leading to the gallery and the second whilst Esther was seated on a chair in the day room. For the first delivery the mother wanted nothing to do with the baby and the already busy nurses had to feed it. Second time around, she was persuaded to suckle the child.

Many of the women with mental problems linked to the birth of their babies had been delivered of their infants prior to admission. Some deliveries appear to have been more strenuous & this may have affected the new mother's well being. In September 1869 Sarah (192/3054) a Leicester dressmaker was admitted due to 'Exhaustion from protracted labour'. The first child that Annie (210/74) was confined of 3 weeks before her admission, was 'said to have been a particularly large one.' Another Annie (211/41) from Market Street Ashby, had also delivered 3 weeks before, but this time her puerperal

---

11   Superintendent's Journal DE3533-85

insanity was believed to be due to the delivery of twins. Many confinements had often taken place in the midst of a poverty stricken way of life. Frances (192/2880) a factory hand from Leicester had married at 18 years of age and had six children during her first six years. Sparse diets within tight budgets were not conducive with a woman's body having the strength to endure a pregnancy coupled with the strength for her body to feed the successive child. Comfort from Husbands Bosworth a mother of three children was a prime example of a poverty stricken mother. She arrived on 25th May 1847 aged 28 and died at the asylum 16th September of the same year: -

'....had been brought very low in consequence of the times, the great scarcity of provisions and the consequent want of them…From the time of this patient's admission up to the period of her death this patient completely absorbed the whole time and attention of one nurse who was obliged to feed her with every portion of food she took - she continued until her decease , noisy, dirty and occasionally violent, indeed but for her physical debility she would have been excessively violent for many weeks she was kept alive with eggs, wine, ale and brandy of which the latter she consumed at least a Gallon.' (185/804)

Forty-six mothers were recorded with supposed cause of malady, 'lactation', 'super lactation', 'debility from lactation', 'protracted lactation', 'over lactation' or the 'demands of suckling'. Lydia (186/926) from Great Glen appears to have developed melancholia as a result of protracted suckling which operated prejudicially upon a weak and previously debilitated frame. Arrangements were made for a boatman's wife (185/796) from Mountsorrel, admitted with puerperal & milk fever, to have her breasts carefully drawn twice a day with emollient poultices placed on them. Mary Ann (187/1503) a lace runner's breasts were in quite a state on admission, 'large milk abscesses - large quantities of milk and purulent matter from the right breast.' One of the mothers had suffered from cholera too. A mother from Lyddington, whose sufferings were due to 'disappointed affections', had suckled her illegitimate child until it was three years old. (187/1389) Rebecca a framework knitter from Littlethorpe was recorded as follows: -

'Eleven months ago she was delivered of a living child which she suckled until about 12 or 14 days before her admission - She has been subjected to great privations of food and clothing during the latter part of her suckling, rather profuse menorrhagia was established. Many days without tasting animal food.' (187/1508)

There were for many households' double sided arrangements to make. Firstly, a home without a mother: Secondly, a newborn to look after without its mother. Some mothers were well enough to miss their babies and or children with Elizabeth (187/1654) from Hemington making '…proper & natural enquiries about her children.'

Harriet (201/5548) from Beresford Street, Coalville became much quieter and rational for a week, then wanted to go home to see her husband and baby, but was not well enough to do so. Some of the mothers were sadly never going to get home to their families again. Nine died within just a few days after admission with 6 of them having cause of death recorded as maniacal exhaustion. Tragically, Mary Ann (192/2933), Maria (191/2632), Elizabeth (2 of them 188/1957 & 186/1264), Eliza (188/1931), Sarah Ann (190/2352), Ruth (192/2897), Caroline (197/4681) all died within a few days of admission. The following conditions were given as their cause of their death - puerperal, acute pneumonia, maniacal exhaustion or maniacal excitement; all of these were linked to childbirth. Ruth (192/2897) of Shenton has the most traumatic story of all. She was admitted dreadfully exhausted after a journey of 14 miles on a bed on a carrier's cart 17th July 1868 and died in the asylum 24th July 1868.

Men by comparison do not appear to have the same extent of mental problems immediately influenced by their gender. But Frederick (200/5340), Charles (204/73), Ernest (204/139), Henry (205/53), Harold (206/120) & William (206/2) were all recorded when admitted as having had problems with their adolescence.

Photographs of Female Patients. Asylum Casebooks courtesy of ROLLR.

Admissions of the elderly

A few hundred of those not expected to get better were those admitted with mental and or physical problems related to old age. For many when it came to achieving a cure, the elderly patients were viewed by some as 'the almost hopeless' at the time of admission. Most were diagnosed as suffering from 'senile dementia' or 'senile mania'. Many on admission must have been just like William admitted from Gilmorton, with senile mania at the age of 86 in 1889: -

'He has not the vaguest notion of his whereabouts.' (198/4938)

In 1849 & 1859 there is mention of the asylum being full which led to several patients being released earlier than normal to make way for more urgent cases. An elderly Mary from Woodhouse Eaves was admitted in February 1846: -

'In consequence of the asylum being too full to receive her at the commencement of the present attack she has necessarily been kept at home, and has been strapped down in an outhouse for the last 7 weeks.' (185/669)

Out of just over seven thousand admissions, the ages were known for approximately six & a half thousand. Taking figures from the known ages over seventeen percent were sixty-one years or over at the time of admission. There were just over 700 between the age of 61 & around 70, over 360 aged between 71 & 80 and there were about 80 aged between the age of 71 & 99. They were the one of the groups of patients admitted to the asylum, who frustrated the doctors, who were trying to promote their 'house of cure', as they were generally viewed as 'incurable'. There was and still is, no cure for old age. There were just over eleven hundred more elderly patients, with many of them suffering from just the same mental conditions as younger residents – with dementia (not specified as senile), some form of mania, idiocy/imbecility and melancholia. Over two hundred elderly patients had the adjective 'senile' or the condition of 'senility' ascribed to their mental condition – Over sixty incoming patients with 'senile dementia': Over sixty with 'senile mania', 4 with 'senile imbecility' & just one with 'senile melancholia'. The term 'senile' was first introduced into the case books on 19th December 1849 when Edward (186/1033) a farmer from Ingleby was admitted with 'senile dementia'. Following Edward, came Isaac (186/1156) a framework knitter, from Bagworth in March 1851 & Jarvis (187/1317) a butcher from Syston in December 1852. There were just the four others from 1851 to 1853, Lydia (186/1145), Sophia (187/1323), Ann (186/1206)& Joseph (186/1187) who were all diagnosed with 'senile imbecility'. George (186/1274) from Loughborough was the youngest at 54 to arrive with senile dementia in 1854. The word 'senile' does not appear to be used again in the casebooks as a condition on admission until eighteen years later when Elizabeth (193/3207) from Aston Flamville is admitted with Senile Dementia in May 1871. The use of the word 'senile' is far more frequent in the closing decades of the 19th Century. Many of the elderly admissions, at least 773 of them eventually died in the asylum, 14 remained as patients or were transferred, & 21 had sections that were blank or had no details. There were 336 more fortunate elderly patients, who were actually cured or noticeably relieved enough to be able to return home.

Photographs of Elderly Patients. Asylum Casebooks courtesy of ROLLR.

Almost three hundred patients had a cause of death that was directly linked to old age, with phrases such as 'senile decay', 'debility & old age' & just pure 'old age'. Nearly a hundred patients who had been admitted with some form of senile mental deficiency, died of 'old age' of some form. There were nine who died of senile decay after treatment for over 30 years: There were three patients admitted in their thirties or forties & one with no known age on admission whose eventual cause of death was 'senile decay'. These patients who actually died in the asylum after treatment for more than forty years were the exception rather than the rule: -

a) John (188/1809) a shopkeeper from Edith Weston had been admitted with melancholia at the age of 37 and died at the asylum 47 years later.

b) Eliza (217/61) was a grocer's wife from London who was admitted with chronic mania at the age of 42 & died there 45 years later.

c) John (217/3) a farm bailiff from Melton was admitted to the asylum aged 45 with chronic mania and died there 42 years later. He had not though been continually confined to the asylum for in December 1880, it was noted that he had to be stopped from rambling into town, 'in consequence of having become very troublesome by going into banks and places'.

d) Thomas (187/1467) who was admitted as a criminal from Leicester Gaol admitted 9th March 1854 & died still a patient in 6th Sept 1898.

Photographs of Elderly Patients. Asylum Casebooks courtesy of ROLLR.

Accidents included as cause of mental illness

As previously noted epilepsy often had its origin in an accident of some kind, but many patients had mental problems believed to be due to just an accident, which did not necessarily involve the onset of epilepsy. There were accidents at work, at home, at school, with vehicles, with animals, with firearms, with water, during sporting activities or as part of failed suicide attempts, which included many records of people 'precipitating themselves through windows'. To take one example Jane (212/105) from Ashby had been involved in a serious accident with a trap just prior to her admission in December 1907. Individuals were also injured when attacked, during fights and James (193/3203) a carpenter from Fleckney, had actually self-mutilated or had voluntarily inflicted himself by purposefully placing his hand under a cartwheel.

Those who had fallen fell in quite a range of ways and most of the fallen, whose falls had resulted in admissions to an asylum, had usually suffered serious injury to their head. A few of them are recorded as having been unconscious for some time afterwards. There were falls from lofts, chimneys, trees, ladders, scaffolding and falls down cellars. There were also incidents of things falling on patients such as iron fenders and trees. Various accidents were caused through involvement with animals. Horses and ponies get far more mention than cows. Thomas (195/4081) from Aylestone had fallen from a pony whilst out hunting with his father as a child. At least six men suffered long-term illness due to a kick from a horses hoof. The most tragically affected was Joseph (186/1043) once a blacksmith from Thurlaston: -

> 'The attack appears to have been the result of concussion of the brain, produced by the kick of a horse he was shoeing - he was confined for a long time to the house and was subjected to a long course of medical treatment, from the time of his accident, he was subject to epilepsy and his fits are of a very severe character, his memory and understanding are tolerably good and his propensities harmless he was discharged from his situation as a blacksmith, his employers who were afraid his fits would subject him to constant and great danger - he subsequently became a hawker of Manchester goods and from his own statement which seemed a reasonable enough was robbed of them as well as his money in a lodging house to which two men the robbers had recommended him, he was afterwards found by the police wandering in the Parish of Thurlaston nearly starved to death - his habits have been very industrious and temperate.'

Certain patients were injured whilst following their trades. Several men from the armed forces had received injuries whilst serving their country. Construction workers, such as masons and bricklayers, suffered injuries from falling themselves, or from their building materials falling upon them. One of the bricklayers was so traumatised by the extent of his injury that he had to be admitted in a strait waistcoat and unfortunately died the next day (193/3392). A locomotive stoker was thrown from an engine (186/1202), on to a railway line and a railway labourer suffered severe mental shock when both his legs were broken (186/1203). These two railway workers were admitted three days apart in August 1851. A printer was knocked on the head by the revolving screen of a printing press in May 1905 (205/39). Colliers worked within very dangerous environments, with Robert (187/1439) from Netherseal having suffered serious injuries following an explosion at his mine. A domestic servant Mary (190/2382) had in 1862 become severely burned & mentally unwell following a gas explosion.

Several of those having to be admitted, had had severe accidents with vehicles. Incoming patients had been crushed between two carts at the sewage works at the Abbey Meadow (187/1562), struck by shafts of carriages (192/2936), fallen from bicycles, knocked down by trams or had fallen from carts or drays. Frederick (196/4323) an imbecile with a congenital defect from Loughborough had actually run into a railway wagon in 1882.

There were also patients who had had accidents with water. John a framework knitter from Thurmaston had several years before his asylum admission nearly lost his life by drowning: -

> '... and it is probable his nervous system has never recovered the shock occasioned by the near and unexpected approach of death.' (186/1165)

Ivor (205/39) from Burton on the Wolds had run into a well on a dark night. A few patients had a history of being involved in a fight or an attack of some kind of scuffles, which led in part to mental illness usually, included a blow to the head. One of the worst cases happened to George of Ratby: -

> '... it appears from the history of this case that this poor man was employed as a night watchman at Meadow Lane near Leeds and that during his rounds one dark night and in a lonely, and unfrequented spot he was suddenly pounced upon by two men who threatened if he offered any resistance, to blow his brains out, the nervous shock consequent upon this unprovoked and savage attack completely prostrated the poor fellow - he lost all consciousness for a time and when he at length partially recovered from the treatment to which he had been brutally subjected his reason was gone... but the local abstraction of blood much relieved him, and gave him sleep at night, to which he had long been a stranger.' (186/905)

Joseph of Newbold Verdon also had quite a tragic story in March 1846: -

> 'Epileptic mania at 12 years of age when wrestling with another lad he received a heavy fall on the back part of the head which was severely fractured he was insensible for some time - At the time of his last attack he was at his usual work in the field when a Gamekeeper came up to him and asked him if he had any snares in his pocket he replied in the negative, the keeper then told him he would shoot him and having loaded his gun with powder only suddenly fired it off at the back of the lad who was quite unprepared for such an act the lad was dreadfully agitated and immediately ran home leaving his coat in the field the maniacal excitement instantly followed upon the above dastardly act - to have 8 leeches applied to the temples - to have 6 leeches applied behind the ears - and cold applications to the head.' (185/678)

Patients had not only suffered serious accidents outdoors, many had also had extreme types of weather to contend with. The most regularly encountered severe weather conditions that led to mental illness were far too much sun. Virtually three dozen patients, were admitted with mental complaints whose initial cause was given as either 'sunstroke' or 'extreme heat'. Some had suffered from intense temperatures whilst in the armed forces. Those not in the forces who had contracted mental weakness through spells of hot weather, were generally outdoor workers such as farmers, farm labourers, graziers, brickyard labourers, coachmen, road men, carters. Young Frederick a biscuit factory worker from Wigston had though suffered from sunstroke when 10 years old : -

'He was most of the day bathing when it was very hot & was a good deal exposed: when he came home with his mother he says he was 'very queer' and partially insensible & had been under 2 doctors for it.' (199/5145)

George (197/4679) a brickyard labourer, had the assigned cause of his complaint, as sunstroke that he had contracted one day. In the evening of the same day it had taken eight men to hold him in his bed. Five days later he died, the cause of death being then given as 'double acute pneumonia'.

It was not only the sunny weather that was guilty of being the cause of insanity. Alveria (185/770) a blacking manufacturer from Loughborough was much affected by an awful thunderstorm 1st August 1846. Sarah (195/3875) from Melton seemed to go right off her head during another thunderstorm in October 1878. George (193/3204) from Sapcote had been said to suffer from occasional epileptic seizures after he had been struck by lightning. Joseph (186/1309) a trimmer from Loughborough who had previously suffered an attack of paralysis from which he recovered, subsequently experienced a great excitation of manner & conduct on the occasion of his dwelling house being flooded by the late heavy rains in December 1852.

John a labourer from Husbands Bosworth had as his supposed cause of malady 'exposure to a whirlwind': -

'..was clearing out a pit & by his masters orders stripped stark naked, while thus engaged a violent whirlwind came & he was exposed for a long time being afraid to go and get his clothes. He suffered retention of urine afterwards and from violent rheumatic pains' (192/2932)

Meteorological conditions appear then to have had a significant impact on peoples' lives, especially when the temperatures hovered around zero. A framework knitter admitted from Hinckley in 1846 is recorded as: -

'The cold weather however which occurred at the commencement of the present year played sad havoc with the aged insane.' (185/728)

Affairs of the Heart & Bereavements which lead to mental ill health

Some of the patients were admitted with the supposed cause of their malady as 'disappointment in love', 'love affairs', 'love attachment', 'anxiety in love affairs', 'crossed in love' & 'love trouble'. Amongst those who were mentally & detrimentally struck by various affairs of the heart was Jane (192/2980) from Blaby who had had disappointment in a matrimonial engagement. Mary a general servant, who arrived from Staffordshire in 1887: -

'When asked why she had come from Birmingham, she replied "To see you darling and to marry you". (198/4811)

Lucy (190/2557) from Clipsham was actually deserted by her sweetheart. Sarah (188/1804) from Ashby's young man had gone to Australia. Louisa (191/2873) from Grantham's brother had stated that her affliction was brought on owing to her having formed an improper intimacy with a banker's son. Florence (203/6074) from Market Harborough had at the age of 19 years old an illegitimate child (now 5 years old) by a young man some two or three years her junior, the young man had marriage forced upon him with another girl for a similar reason. Florence was understandably most upset & melancholic by this marriage and had even attempted to drown herself. Elizabeth (187/1345) from Heather had been seduced by her master who had promised to marry her. After she was confined of twins, her master deserted her and she consequentially became very gloomy & desponding. Relatives were not always ready to assist members of their families, when they got in the family way. May from Loughborough formerly a nursery governess, was recorded as: -

> 'She took up with an organ grinder & got in the family way was disowned by her aunt & sent to the Loughborough Workhouse where she was confined of a male child.' (211/76)

Another lady (210/145) from Asfordby had given birth to an illegitimate, female, child. The mother of this baby girl became very worried as the father just disappeared & could not be found. Sarah Ann (196/4234) from Loughborough appeared to have had delusions about a married man wishing to marry her, she said she saw on a wall paper with these five capitals on it and the meaning was (M.C.S.A.L) 1Marriage 2C (the man's surname starting with C) 3 Sarah 4 Ann 5 L (her surname starting with L) numbers written high and above.

Photograph of part of the doctor's entry sheet within the Case/Books for patient 196/4234. Courtesy of ROLLR.

Some of the patients had appeared to become insane due to exceptional family circumstances. William (196/4230) the painter from Market Harborough was much aggrieved by his daughter running away to get married. Elizabeth (195/4063) a hosiery seamer from Shepshed was shocked and aggrieved at her brother marrying a girl long pregnant. Another Elizabeth (192/2879) from Ratcliffe Culey was very despondent when her daughter left for Australia. Phoebe (186/948) from Peatling Parva was broken hearted after her favourite son left for America. Sarah (191/2611) from Sileby was upset when her son left home to become a soldier.

Many more suffered melancholic grief when family members died. Joseph (204/39) a sinker maker suffering with mania from Loughborough had four children living, but had lost five within 12 hours of birth. There is also the case of the blacksmith & his wife from Markfield, William (202/5901-205/21) & Maria (186/1289-190/2297-190-2426-192-3014), who were both admitted to the asylum several times & who had been bereaved of all their six young babies or children.[12] Parents also grieved through losing their off springs in adulthood such as Robert (189/2016) a gardener who had lost three of his family in adulthood within 15 months.

Francis had had 5 children, who all died soon after birth. Ann from Bottesford had lost her son in an accident. Another Ann from Syston aged 81 had been admitted with melancholia her elderly mother only having died just a year before her admission. A mother from Gilmorton was told a week before her admission in July 1901, of the death of her son (a soldier in Egypt) & soon after she became very mentally unbalanced, 'Crying out for her boy.' Mary from the Canal bank Loughborough had lost her fourth child 2 years before admission through "overlying it" and was overwhelmed by the fact that it was her fault. A mother from Kibworth Beauchamp (194/3716) believed that she was the reason why her infant had died from convulsions in 1876. Ann (187/1581) from Earl Shilton was also overwhelmed with guilt, 'She has confessed that the circumstances of her having given by mistake some laudanum to her child, which she believes caused its speedy death has preyed upon her mind.

There were periods when major infectious diseases were unfortunately rife, often resulting in the deaths of family members of all ages. Betsy from Croxton Kerrial was admitted in 1854 with the supposed cause of her mental condition to be 'maternal anxieties', she was 'extremely fond of her children, of whom two have recently died of scarlet fever.

For other patients it was the loss of their partners that drove them to the darkest mental depths. A couple from Ullesthorpe had a virtual double tragedy as the husband had probably poisoned himself (this is queried in the case books) & died the day after his wife's admission. The wife Julia died seven days later from maniacal exhaustion. Naomi from Loughborough admitted with 'confusional insanity' in January 1904, is recorded as follows: -

> 'She refuses to recognise that her husband is dead & persists in going to be with his dead body & has now continued acting in this manner for fourteen hours. Wrapped the body in hot blankets, hot bottles to feet, pan of hot crock to face, drank brandy & breathed into his nostrils to revive him & got into bed with the body.' (211/31)

---

12 Inscription on the family Grave in Markfield Cemetery

Hannah from Leicester's mind had become 'completely unhinged' after the loss of her husband. Another Hannah who was quite elderly was also obviously distraught following the death of her husband: -

> 'Has been in a workhouse about 9 weeks. Was sent there because she was wandering about the village and making herself a nuisance to the inhabitants by continually crying out for "Chris". Her husband whose name was "Chris" has been dead four or five months and this is supposed to be the cause of her trouble.' (212/83)

Peter (195/4068) an Irish labourer from Ballaghadarren County Mayo, had created quite a crowd of onlookers when he was found kneeling praying for his wife who had died a couple of years before & all his children, who were at home in Ireland in a workhouse.

If it was not immediate partners then it was other close family members especially the parents. A housewife from Station Street in Loughborough was overwhelmed with grief when her mother died: -

> 'Her mother died 11 days ago and the day after patient became very wild & excited - wanted to go into the coffin too. Says she was the sister to Baden Powell & Burglar Dunn that the Queen was her mother - Wraps herself up in blankets and sprawls on the floor with her bedding on top. Gets worse mentally is more like a wild beast in conduct than a human being is a most miserable object to appearance.' (203/6153)

Fielding Johnson Building. Courtesy of University of Leicester Archives.

Martha (189/2266) from Binley, did not become ill until the death of her mother. Elizabeth from Hoby after her father died, took it very much to heart.: -

> 'She buried her wedding ring deep down in the middle of the earth as she thought it would be safe there. She used to lie for hours on her fathers grave, as he was the only friend she had'. (203/6078)

Ursula (210/15) from Tugby informed the asylum staff that she would go to the Church Yard where she talked to her mother. For some it was the tragic circumstance of multiple family losses such as in the case of Patience (200/5329) from Earl Shilton who lost her mother and a few days later one of her children too. James (187/1372) a corn factor lost his wife & two children within a couple of months of each other. At times it was the death of a special friend that is given as the supposed cause of their mental unrest. Naomi (212/71) from Melton Mowbray had had news of the death of her best friend in South Africa just four days before her admission with mania in May 1907.

Previous occupations which aggravated an individual's mental health

Having an occupation was one of the priorities of life. It was amongst other things a reputation within one's immediate society. The only inmates having no trace of a profession at all were usually the 'idiots' or 'imbeciles'. It appears at times, that the occupational thread of life, played a major part in the patient's mental disturbance, especially when they gradually or suddenly became unfit for work. No work usually meant no salary. Joseph (186/964) a shoemaker was just one of many who was under the idea that he was unfit to practise his business. John (194/3504) a signalman had the assigned cause of his mental condition to be 'over work,' as he was frequently required to work many hours at a stretch. A baker's wife (211/43) from Edith Weston was rather hard worked, as her husband was inclined to intemperance & she was continually left in charge of the Post Office. There is one case recorded where one incoming patient is noted as having received some form of support within her working environment before admission – Elizabeth (211/26) a factory hand, from Great Bowden, 'who was lodging in Leicester, had some form of hysterical fit & was taken to her rooms in an ambulance.'

Many inmates were recorded with relatively more 'unsettled' occupations such as service men, boatmen, bricklayers, builders, grooms, butlers, cab drivers, carriers, carters, cattle dealers, coachmen, commercial travellers, domestics, drovers, footmen, gamekeepers, gardeners, governesses, hawkers, journeymen, railway labourers, road labourers, seaman, a steward on board 'SS Irvine', a travelling musician, a travelling actor & a travelling jeweller. A man from Rugby (204/109), who had travelled the county in a van with a photographic booth in December 1902, ended up developing mania. George Ernest (203/6089) who had been born in Liverpool stated that he had been in service as a cook on a steamer and also a hotel porter. The unsettled occupations should surely include those that took individuals away from their homes. Ethel (202/5757) went to be a scullery maid in London but the work was too much for her. Working away from home could take some future patients away from the most dedicated & immediate source of support, their families. Sarah Ellen from Coalville had suffered from mental illness before & her subsequent appointment, as a 'nurse probationer' in Yorkshire was sadly unsuccessful.

> 'Been well since her discharge & took to nursing in a general hospital in Sheffield, the authorities noticed she was peculiar & sent her home.' (212/136)

Some, who were working away from their families & were taken ill, were fortunately well enough to realise, that they needed to go home. Ellen (211-98) employed as a schoolteacher, wired her sister at Billesdon in March 1905, to say that she was arriving to stay with her. Another lady whose home town was Hinckley, had been working as a school mistress in Kent for eight years & had kept well until the Christmas before her admission in March 1905. She had suffered from influenza & anaemia and consequentially got very run down. There seemed to be a wave of teachers suffering from mental strain, during the early 1900's for a Marie Annie (210/113), from Ashby who was also a schoolteacher, working in Leicester, suddenly began to talk about taking her own life & had to be taken home. Josephine a governess from Melton Mowbray, who was ultimately discharged relieved, after a four month period of treatment, & taken to Limerick Workhouse, had the following inclusion on admission in March 1902: -

> 'Her own account. - Came to Melton Mowbray from Ireland on the 20th inst in reply to an advertisement for a governess at the Convent School. She put up a hotel and began to drink hard & was in consequence refused the appointment.' (210/62)

Another young lady named Annie had also come over from Ireland to take up a position as a servant in a convent at New Parks and just like Josephine from Limerick she was quite quickly mentally ill: -

> 'Came from Ireland 14 days ago & entered as a domestic the Dane Hill Convent Leicester. Three days ago she appeared to change & began to pray a good deal. Complained of headache 2 days ago. Slept badly took her food badly the last 3 days. At the convent persons are allowed "2 hours recreation" which means they are allowed to talk.' (212/103)

Walter (204/87) had been a 2nd class boy on board the 'Impregnable', in July 1901 where he became an ordinary seaman. When out on shore leave he contracted syphilis and soon after that time he became excited and was 'incessantly talking in a grandiose style'.

During the years when the asylum was operating, having a job was paramount. Once childhood days were over, usually by the age of 12 or 13 if not earlier, young individuals knew that their continued successful existence required them to have an occupation. It was within their general future expectations that they might well have to leave home to get a job. For some there was the paper work & legalities of taking up an apprenticeship for others it was just working away. Several individuals had weak family foundations within relationships, due to family deaths or illegitimacy. For those working as long-term employees, in other people's residences, the away location had become their main contact point, their virtual home. A governess aged 52 from Stapleton: -

> 'Has lately been run down in health & 2 weeks ago came to stay at her former employers house in Stapleton.' (212/79)

There is one admission for a lady named Lucy (212/26) who had been a housekeeper for a gentleman named Henry Griffin in Countess Street, Leicester. She had no relatives listed for contact, just a friend Mr Griffin, so it is highly probable that it was in gratitude for her service, that Mr Griffin transferred her to 'private class' just 5 days later. Elizabeth from Leicester developed mania following the death of her master: -

'In consequence of the sudden death of her master a clergyman in whose family she had
lived for ten years, and the consequent disruption of the Establishment…she was much
esteemed by the family, with whom she had lived so long, and her agony was intense at
the dreadful bereavement.' (186/1113)

The 'sedentary' occupations appeared to cause the same degree of difficulty as the 'unsettled'
occupations. The more static occupations could be listed as lace makers, ribbon weavers, framework
knitters and leather workers. There were other inherent problems within these occupations a
Thomas (198/4857) had severely strained his eyes through working at the frame with as small a light
as he could. At least the bag hosiery agents had given Thomas work for his frame. Poor James was in
a far more tragic employment situation, he was actually having to do the women's tasks: -

'He has had no stocking work for 5 years and that he seams when at home as he is not
able to get to a frame.' (196/4156)

There were problems within certain other types of occupation too. There was George (185/746) the
general porter who was constantly exposed to the cold & wet. William (186/1001) the cab driver was
also exposed to great changes in temperature and much night work. Mary (185/888) a nurse suffered
from 'loss of rest' within her professional tasks. Ann from Leicester was accustomed to spending
many hours in the fields as a labourer, together with having a large family to bring up. Thomas
(186/1237) an 'overlooker of test labour' at a Union Workhouse, was an exceptionally conscientious
worker & his habits had always been active, industrious, and temperate. He stated that for some
time he had not been doing his work to his own satisfaction, even though his master was completely
satisfied with his work. Some of the patients' former occupations took place within extreme and
hazardous environments. George (194/3466) a tramp from Shepshed, admitted with chronic mania in
June 1874, had had his sight seriously impaired due to an accident whilst being employed as a filer in
Sheffield. There was Francis the collier: -

'A good part of that life has been passed in the bowels of the earth, far from the
light of the sun, and it was curious to see the high inflammation set up in his eyes,
in consequence of the unaccustomed glare of light as soon as he became one of the
denizens of the earth.' (186/980)

Benjamin (195/4029) also a collier was lowered too quickly and suddenly down a coalmine and had
appeared to experience a great shock in the process. Accidents at work also took their toll on the
relatives too. A lady from Woodville was admitted with melancholia in May 1849 following a serious
event at a local pit: -

'This patient's nervous system has been much shocked, and her mind depressed by the
loss of two, or three of her family, by shocking accidents in the coal pits in which they
worked, and there is no doubt that these unfortunate circumstances have been the cause
of her mental affliction.' (186/955)

Ann a mother from Overseal is admitted in 1874 with acute mania due to: -

'Domestic trouble her son who works in a pit was brought home much burned and
disfigured and she was much occupied day and night nursing him.' (194/3505)

A William (197/4480) had received a severe blow to his head whilst at Mountsorrel Granite Quarries. Edward (197/4520) whilst 'performing some blasting operation' at a stone quarry in 1884, suffered horrendous injuries (which included destroying the sight of both his eyes). John (204/55) a chimney sweep & Primitive Methodist, from Oakham, went up one chimney, but would not come down again as he had found the Lord up there, 'The Lord told him not to lay up treasures on earth where moth & rust both corrupt.' Some workers created dangers in what were otherwise comparatively safe environments. Alice (197/4787) from Kirby Muxloe, had when in service handled a gun whilst cleaning a room & the gun had gone off and 'frightened her a good deal'. Annie (212/55) a domestic servant had become strange after 'she had accidentally knocked her head against a marble mantelpiece.' Working as both a nurse & a domestic, Sarah Ann (212/73) from Melton, was believed to have been affected by 'a cornice pole falling on her head.'

One of the occupations, which appeared to most readily result with mental problems, was as a member of the armed services. Servicemen had travelled with their various units all over the world to places such as Boulogne (1814-193/3315), Cyprus (197/4631), Egypt (197/4631), Afghanistan (1878-197/4791 & 205/127), Crimea (191/2832), Hong Kong (202/5784), South Africa (204/89 &205/3), Malta (205/46), Bermuda (206/13), and Guernsey (206/17) with ten patients having India listed as their location in service[13]. Josiah (195/3901) from Loughborough and Charles (197/4631) from Wigston were both recorded as being invalided out of their roles within the armed services. Having an immediate relationship with the tools of war, had very evidently had a long term profound effect on Frederick who was formerly a soldier in the artillery, and was admitted in June 1901: -

> '6 weeks ago he was found in an almost moribund condition lying in the road between Newton & Measham, he was cold and stiff and only breathed occasionally - Says he has more shot & shell than anyone, says he will have the white flag & has been killed & many times hurt but is not dead yet.' (204/21)

Certain conditions were picked up whilst in service, such as sunstroke, malaria, ague, deafness and venereal diseases such as gonorrhoea & syphilis; many of these conditions seemed understandably to have contributed to an individual's mental illness

As could be expected there were the problems between the employers and employees with considerable differences of opinion between those in service and their employers. There were unruly and idle youngsters such as William (186/1292) who grew up to an apprenticeship in coach making to become an insubordinate workman and cause havoc within a coach maker's yard. There were also the inappropriate sexual relationships between master & maids. Harriett (212/123) who had been admitted in 1908, at the age of 60, had her named contact to be 'the Master of Loughborough Union'. She was recorded as being an 'illegitimate child her mother having been under the employment of a clergyman.' Elizabeth (194/3710) who was housemaid to one of the hospital visitors had 'got round to brandishing knives at the cook', making absurd noises and eventually disturbing the whole household. John (196/4170) a corn driller of Thorpe Satchville had been reprimanded for faulty workmanship. William a shepherd from Great Bowden believed he had lost his master's sheep & would never be able to recover them: -

> 'The idea was merely the result of a highly excited imagination and had not the slightest foundation.' (185/868)

---

13 Asylum Case Books Records DE3533 (194/3483-199/5163-206/107-204/86-201/5408-201/5581-199/5009-205/127-203/6135-205/52)

Francis (192/2926) an under gamekeeper for Lord Stamford, whose assigned cause of illness was from working in the sun, was afraid that he had not reared enough pheasants and was also under the impression that they had not grown properly.

There were also the worries of professions not thriving. There was the gradual failure of George's (186/1163) trade as a hostler, which he believed, was a 'consequence of the general introduction of the railways'. There were many other professions, which suffered from lack of business, or a slump in trade. One of the worst jobs of all was actual unemployment itself, or the dread of it. An engine fitter (195/4042) from New Donington, who was a member of the Plymouth Brethren, had apparently 'been unemployed for many weeks even though he often had been taken to be tried.' George (204/90) a widower admitted with mania, had formerly been an engine driver on the Midland Railway, but had had no work for 5-6 years & was 'forced to live chiefly on clubs.' A gamekeeper Joseph (187/1618) 'lost his situation from neglect of duty'. A large factory fire (probably at the framework knitting shop of Nottingham Manufacturing Limited in Factory Street[14]) in Loughborough in 1887, left John (198/4937) and William (198/4919) both framework knitters without work. A workhouse schoolmaster (204/35) lost his situation after striking his pupils. Joseph (204/135) from Shepshed became 'depressed through the stoppage of work at the shoe factory where he was employed'. A warehouseman William (204/115) was dismissed from his post after mixing up stockings in different sizes. The Falcon Works at Loughborough dismissed two of its workers, both named William. One had been in charge of an electric crane & was sent home when 'he started up two electric cranes to meet each other, fortunately the event was seen and the current was turned off' (205/102). The other William (205/65), a labourer, was dismissed for striking another workman whom he believed was insulting his parentage. Enoch (200/5264) a river man was perhaps a man before his time in 1892, as he believed 'he lost his employment through a stagnation of the world.' Employers passing away often also resulted in a lack of employment for their employees. Arthur (205/18) who was rather eccentric, had worked as an architect and a teacher, but a disastrous holiday in Blackpool, due to a lack of cash caused by his extravagances, eventually ended up in him being admitted with mania.

Elizabeth (186/1155) admitted as a resident of the Leicester Union workhouse clearly had her condition aggravated by 'the crowded factory conditions and vitiated atmosphere to which she had been exposed to, resulting in pulmonary disease and predisposing her to insanity'. It was not just the factory environments, which caused a problem - Henry the Chief Audit Clerk at Derby Railway also had problems with the office where he worked: -

> '... and has for a long time past been in the habit of sitting engaged in the necessary business of the office, in a very badly ventilated room, of which he has frequently complained , this with close confinement and the sedentary nature of his employment produced great pain in the head, giddiness, sickness, loss of appetite.' (185/830)

A patient's need to be admitted was at times blamed on their sedentary occupation before admission. John a framework knitter was recorded, as: -

> 'The poor man has been accustomed to work very bright scarlet colours in the manufacture of the articles peculiar to his trade and this circumstance added to great anxiety of mind.' (185/689)

---

14   Google Search Engine

Ann's (185/656) weaving of ribbons appears also to have contributed to her mental disease. Quite opposite to the sedentary occupations were those, which supposedly caused too much excitement, as appears to be the case with Robert an actor, formerly a soldier from Baker Street in Leicester: -

> 'Occupation there is but little doubt that the excitement of a soldiers life and subsequently his passion for the histrionic act have proved too powerful stimulants for a mind possessing but a very little calibre.' (185/684)

One of the other causes of the mental maladies, which often necessitated admission to an asylum, was the result of extreme privations. Several were described as 'living hard'. Becoming a pauper usually meant admission to the local Union Workhouse. The inmates had various reasons for straitened circumstances, financial losses or worries. Stagnation within certain trades caused a considerable degree of distress. William a framework knitter from Burbage, who was admitted in July 1847, had the following inclusion within his case book history: -

> 'This man is a Greenwich pensioner, but lately has been employed in the stocking frame at Hinckley, it is supposed that his habits have not been very temperate, although they have been industrious, there is no doubt however that the late stagnation of trade, and the privations, and distress of the working classes generally in this country have tended not a little to aggravate, if not altogether produce mental disorder under which he is now labouring...' (185/825)

It was not just urban distress, working for example with machines in factories, there were also various family insolvencies caused by 'the present agricultural distress' in March 1851.[15] Thomas (185/841) a farmer was deeply concerned that, 'he was a ruined man and should never be able to raise seed to sow his land.' Many of the skilled workers often had two worries. Firstly, their trade and secondly their land (either rented or owned) which would help supplement their income.

Several faced insolvencies within their own businesses with William (206/137) a brick maker from Donisthorpe having to face the failure of his own brickyard. John (191/2640) from Lutterworth who worked within woollen manufacture had become bankrupt. For others like William (185/789) a cigar trader from Loughborough, there could be a large disappointment in business. Elizabeth (201/5511) & her husband from the Canal Bank in Loughborough who were in the fish trade had hardly managed to make a living, through having to cope with severe competition. Charles (205/93) from Great Bowden a hawker had serious business worries no doubt caused by his many debts. Julia (200/5389) a widow from Packington, had for 10 years been gaining a living by selling articles from a handcart. John (186/947) a blacksmith from Knossington, fared badly from a competitor springing up in his own village, who was able to charge more moderately. Emily (194/3713) from Swannington who was a patient admitted with melancholia had had to cope with the family privations caused by 'a lock out at a local pit'. Samuel (191/2817) a cattle drover had been thrown out of work owing to an outbreak of cattle plague in 1868.

---

15   DE3533/186/1154 Noted in a Patient's Case Book

Sometimes a whole town like Market Harborough was suffering from a depressed state in the trade, so individuals such as Thomas (186/1179) a collar maker 'had experienced pecuniary losses and much disappointment'. William (191/2741) from Blaby was short of money when 'he lost the Blaby tollgate, which he had held for some time'. John (206/81) a Kibworth Beauchamp villager, owned a small cottage & garden, but the District Council took over the road & the owner of properties adjacent to those roads was expected to pay the costs for making up those same roads. James (186/1277) who had the dual occupations of publican and joiner became so extremely anxious about his business 'that they ultimately became the sole subject for his thoughts'. Elizabeth the Leicester Register Office Keeper for Servants had family problems of a more unusual nature: -

> 'The attack came on about 10 days ago in its more violent form but long antecedent to that period the patient had been unusually excited without any apparent cause except that of having resigned to her daughter the management of her usual business, the keeping of the Register Office for servants, it is not at all improbable that the want of her former employment, added to the very natural anxiety she would feel to her daughter's success may be fairly adduced as the exciting causes of the present attack - derived marked relief from the use of opiates.' (185/872)

At times financial problems causing mental illness were not always directly linked to an occupation. A publican from Leicester named Thomas (185/687), had sudden unforeseen good fortune. This situation was just too much for him and he took to drinking ardent spirits in a raw state. A few incoming patients had money difficulties within the family. James (186/919) a day labourer from Orton on the Hill, suffered from insanity brought on by his son's reckless extravagance. Ann a clergyman's wife from Swepstone (admitted in 1848) is recorded as follows: -

> '... she has of late been exposed to privations by the bursting of a bubble Life Assurance Company, whereby she was suddenly deprived of those necessaries and comforts to which she had hitherto been accustomed...' (185/851)

Mary (191/2700) a widow from Woodhouse with seven children, had lost her husband several years before admission to the asylum and being left with such a large family, struggled to maintain them and whilst doing so 'over tasked her energies'. Jane (185/829) from Quorndon who died in the asylum from pneumonia, was an assistant to her husband who was a gardener, during this time 'she was frequently exposed to sudden and severe alternations of temperature', which had no doubt exercised a most pernicious influence on her health. Thomas (185/660) a gentleman from Lincolnshire was in a virtually opposite position as he is recorded as being able to enjoy all the comforts and many of the luxuries of life as he was 'united to a wife whose sole study has been his happiness'.

The Chapel. Stewart Collection courtesy of ROLLR.

Religious excitement as a probable cause of mental illness

Religious beliefs played a major part in the lives of almost all of the patients being admitted. If lives were not centred on worship & beliefs then they were usually lived in fear of the devil. Eliza (212/1) of Billesdon, 'Declared the devil was concealed within her bed…praying & rushing about looking for the devil.' Samuel (185/822) a butcher from a village in Lincolnshire, ' … fancied that the Devil had got hold of him and that he should go to hell for his crimes…' William (185/848) a warp hand from Quorndon - 'He entertains the grossest delusions on the subject of religion, his conversation when questioned on the subject, being principally connected with his satanic majesty.' Ann (186/1040) a collier's wife from Melton was, 'totally dammed.' A housewife from Loughborough (211/51) was recorded as follows, 'Says the devil has told her to go to hell & she is going into the vortex.'

Far more incoming patients were seeking salvation, which they felt would be found within their individual religious beliefs & that is why they directed a considerable proportion of their energies towards them. Alice (211/66) from Oakham may have felt that her vicar could rescue her from her mental trauma, for she had threatened to drown herself, when individuals tried to keep her away from the local vicarage. A butler called Edward from Sheepy Lodge, Sheepy: -

'Yesterday morning at 5.30 knocked up the Rector-got the church keys-places primroses on the altar & afterwards refused to give up the keys.' (206/73)

Laura was from a family with many illegitimate children & was admitted from Market Harborough Police Station as she had attracted the clergy's attention in a disgraceful way. She wrote several abusive letters to them, accusing them of scandalous behaviour: -

'She was reported to the police, but managed to evade arrest on account of her wandering vagabond life, which she led until this morning, when she was found out by the road & brought in.' (December 1904) (211/84)

Around two hundred patients were just too wrapped up with their religion, whatever that might be and this was reputed to be the actual supposed cause of their mental malady. Almost half of those, whose mental condition was related to their individual spiritual beliefs, were thought to be suffering from the effects of 'religious excitement'. Others were recorded with 'religious anxiety', 'religious enthusiasm', 'religious despondency', 'religious impressions', 'religious mania' or 'religious melancholy'. Intense religious feelings were also experienced in the form of delusions or illusions. John (186/989) a shoemaker from Leicester actually imagined himself to be the almighty. Thomas a labourer from Billesdon: -

'…He entertains the notion that he is sent by Christ to preach the gospel to all the world and under this impression he has carried the bible about with him and has collected people together to whom he has ministered.' (187/1339)

Thomas a brick maker from Hinckley is recorded, 'Frequently he is in a state of great exaltation which he declares to be the result of direct interposition of the Holy Spirit.' (189/2220)

William a bricklayer from Castle Donington complained of pains in his head due to him being: -

'Too much engaged in the work of God.' (194/3587)

Edward (206/49) a general labourer from Lutterworth: - 'God has sent me to be a nuisance on earth.' Caroline (212/47) a hosiery hand from Gladstone Street in Loughborough was recorded: - 'Quotes hymns and talks wildly about the "Belief", the "Divinity" and colours red, white & blue.' Bertha (212/53) from Sileby was reputed to have heard a voice from heaven & 'to have seen the Lord in the clouds.' Charlotte from Barrow on Soar informed the doctor on admission that: -'…. she is going to heaven to scrub the floors.' (210/3) Alice from Hinckley believed she was having problems at home believing: - '..That her sisters are acting under divine instructions, & she therefore submits'. (210/5) Alice from Hinckley believed: - 'That she was the true vine & was soon to become a martyr. She often held communion with the Virgin Mary.' (211/49)

A hosiery mender from Hinckley named Alice was seriously religiously deluded: -

> 'Says she is going to die - the pilgrims are waiting for her; she is going to join her brother in Paradise - The Lord told her last night that she is to come to him at once.' (212/96)

A bricklayer from Bakehouse Lane in Lutterworth, started going up on the roof of his house to preach (189/2254). On that same roof he had taken some slates off & nailed the deeds of his house down under them. Florence (211/134) from Birstall had exhibited one Sunday an unusual religious fervour asking those about her 'to be prepared for their future.' Susannah (210/140) from Hugglescote's believed her future was no more as she had been there to hear her own funeral sermon. James a shepherd from Kibworth Harcourt had a quite complex religiously linked delusion: -

> 'He also has some absurd delusions such as fancying that he died 5 years ago having exchanged his life for a supernatural power which he says now dwells in his body and makes him appear alive.' (192/2847)

James a publican & joiner from Loughborough was severely afflicted with his religious beliefs: -

> 'At the present time his melancholy appears to be now triggered with religious enthusiasm than when he was first admitted, his Bible is rarely out of his hand… after many elaborate attempts at suicide succeeded on the 21st July in strangling himself by means of a strip sheet fastened to the handle of his dormitory window.' (186/1303)

The atheists within the asylum must have been on their guard, as in 1861 David a labourer from Earl Shilton believed that: -

> 'He had a commission from God to destroy all unbelievers.' (189/2242)

Certain other daily occupations or pursuits had also caused problems with mental stability. A couple of patients had become over excited within their roles as local Wesleyan preachers. Young Sarah (187/1358) had been a servant for a family who had professed high Calvinistic doctrines and suffered from the effects of being compelled by the mistress of the house, to attend 'her' place of worship – whose 'her' is not made clear. Richard (206/78) from Wymeswold was initially admitted under the belief, that he was to be the asylum chaplain and he never thought that he was entering the asylum as a lunatic. He had been wearing clerical garb for many years and had preached or addressed at Adult Schools. He was a compelling letter writer & whilst an asylum patient he wrote to the Committee & Home Secretary begging of them, to let him have his discharge and he also wrote a letter to offer himself as a highly suitable candidate for the post of Chaplain at the New Asylum at Narborough.[16]

---

16   See copy of letter Page 69.

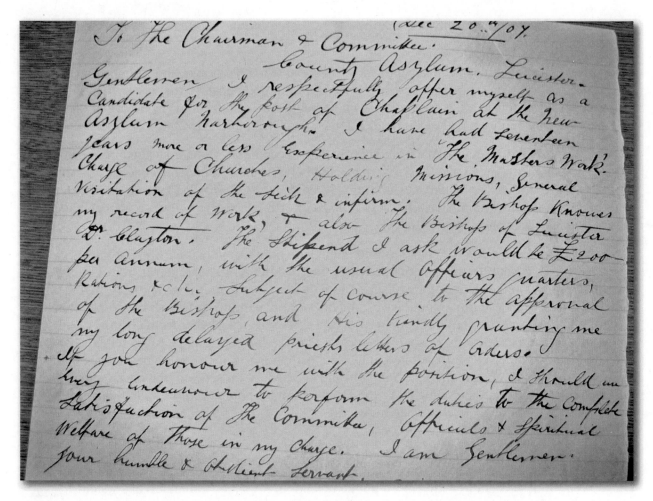

Photograph of a letter written by one of the patients (206/78) still within the case books at the Leicestershire County Record Office. Courtesy of ROLLR.

A few patients were admitted in consequence of being religiously excited by a variety of events. Gertrude (210/79) from Bagworth had been confirmed about 4 years ago, and soon after had hysterical fits of screaming. John (187/1582) a shoemaker by trade developed sudden, acute mania as the result of a discussion he had heard from his minister. A dissenter & hosiery worker named Mary Jane (212/7) from Leicester had begun travelling out to Countesthorpe to revival meetings there, prior to being admitted with mania. Thomas (190/2428) a labourer had been seriously affected by a revival going on in his neighbourhood of Langton, where he had become a promoter. Ellen from Kibworth Harcourt: -

'Has been attending mission services about a month ago & seemed excited by them. A fortnight ago her mistress gave her notice on account of her impertinence but as her impertinence became more marked she was dismissed 6 days ago. Went to stay with a friend & while there said she was a bride packed up things out of the kitchen & said they were hers.' (211/15)

Martha a lace runner from Ironville in Derbyshire, suffered serious ill effects after listening to a ranter's sermon: -

> 'This is a case of melancholia which came on about two months ago, almost immediately after an attendance at a Ranter's discourse, one of those appeals to the passions, rather than to the judgement of the auditory, where people are sent without rhyme or reason to everlasting perdition and excommunication is freely dealt out '. (186/946)

Mary (200/5267) a Roman Catholic from Shepshed had become over excited when a Roman Catholic Mission had come to her village. There were a couple of occasions where conversions to another faith may have caused mental unrest. Elizabeth (188/1747) from Barrow had recently converted to Catholicism just before admission. One lady from Kegworth (195/3841) really reproached herself after leaving Church and going to Chapel.

Several patients before admission had caused immediate family or neighbourhood problems due to their less sociable, yet extreme religious activities. Joseph (189/2100) a bricklayer from Lutterworth, had been praying in the streets of his village at 1 or 2 o'clock in the morning. Thomas (189/2131) a mole catcher from Billesdon, would have gone out without clothing to preach the gospel, if his friends had not prevented him from doing so. John (186/996) a tea hawker from Grimston had quite an unusual reason for the onset of his mental illness, which was linked, to his religious beliefs. He had for some time been engaged in writing for a prize to be awarded to the best essay on 'the perpetual and divine obligation to the Sabbath' and he only just missed winning the competition. The resulting disappointment, which was 'the extinction of his hopes', produced all the unhappy consequences from which he eventually suffered.

It was not just excitement within religion that may have caused mental ill health. Mary from Leicester (admitted in 1846) had developed 'impulsive insanity', which was supposedly brought: -

> 'As a result of fright by witnessing a public execution, the shock to the nervous system was so great as almost to cause death'. (185/718)

As well as public executions there were the Chartist disturbances of 1848, to view and three patients were recorded as being affected by this form event (185/873-185/882-186/1107). William the rope maker was most deeply affected: -

> 'Constantly uttering the most blasphemous language, his excitement then was caused by the chartist riots and he had an impression that the strike of the operatives and the disturbances consequent there on would establish Chartism in place of the law of the land, and that an equal division of property would take place.' (186/1107)

George (206/69) a roadman from Orton on the Hill had been at work up until a few days before his admission but he got excited in some recent political event and was worried because the candidate he was interested in was not elected. It was not just national political enthusiasms there were the international ones too, which reached the lives of the asylum inmates. Julius (186/1231) the furrier from Denmark, admitted in December 1851, was recorded as having the cause of his mental excitement being the French Revolution; he was subsequently removed to Denmark in the care of his friends.

Within the casebook records, there are some of the sadder incidences noted where several of the patients were linked to some form of sexual mal practise. Edward (203/6171) from Gilmorton had been convicted for indecently assaulting a female. Most of the inappropriate sexual behaviours involved adults and under age youngsters. Joseph according to his wife was: - 'prone to meddling with little girls and he had an unnatural lust after them'. (195/4030)

Frederick (206/18) from Burbage had also taken to interfering with young girls. Thomas (200/5219) from Market Harborough had been exposing himself before young girls and Edward (218/345) from Snibston in July 1893 was taken up for committing an unnatural offence on a boy. James (189/2056) a teacher at Roman Catholic Reformatory, admitted as an asylum patient, had been charged with improper behaviour to some boys in his charge. At times the assaults had taken place within the family. Charles (203/6135) from Broughton Astley tried to have connection with his youngest daughter 'because he believed it was necessary, as some girls come to maturity earlier than others'. Sarah (198/4915) from Smeeton Westerby had a father who was at present doing several months hard labour for tampering indecently with his daughter. It is unclear if the daughter was actually Sarah.

Intemperance as a cause of mental illness

The intemperate were far more likely to be troublesome within their immediate environments than those suffering from religious excitement. Too much alcohol was also often the likely cause of unrest within family life. Francis a farmer from Cottesmore was one of the few patients who were recorded as through intemperance, having fallen back to a virtual animal state: -

> '...It is quite clear that it is useless to trust him again, society is shocked, the lives of his family endangered by his brutal and drunken orgies, he is as treacherous as he is dangerous and constantly requires the most careful supervision...whenever there is an opportunity to get at drink, no matter of what kind, or in what quantity, his Guardian angel deserts him, his animal propensities get the better of his moral and intellectual faculties and he becomes worse than a beast.' (185/1168)

Joseph from Cadeby had followed a similar intemperate pattern: -

> 'Intemperance for some months past, he has been residing from home at a watering place where he has been in the habit of drinking the waters to great excess, he has been squandering his property in the purchase of most ridiculous articles which he did not want and could not use...' (185/826)

Virtually ten percent of the patient admissions to Leicestershire County Lunatic Asylum were admitted due to excessive alcohol consumption. 'Intemperance' is a word in exceptionally constant use throughout the case notes. There were various types of alcohol that individuals were drawn to with Elizabeth (187/1474) from Leicester Union having 'indulged herself in whatever stimulating drinks she could attain'. Mary (213/7) from Sileby was 'addicted to drinking whiskey'. Hannah (185/664) from Loughborough the wife of a boatman was defined as an abandoned character and 'had again addicted herself to excessive indulgence in both spirituous and malt liquors'. Andrew (217/189) from Somerby is recorded as 'drinking much latterly - mixing all kinds of fluids together'.

Arthur (192/3010) a shoe finisher from Leicester was 'much addicted to the habit of self-pollution'. One of the incoming patients (212/117) was recorded as, 'Used to drink secretly'. It was not just alcoholic intemperance, for Sarah (188/1803) a blacksmith's wife from Woodhouse Eaves was recorded as suffering from 'intemperance in the use opium'. Ann (185/862) from Empingham, who had followed her husband who was a soldier, even out as far as the West Indies, had addicted herself to intemperance & large quantities of snuff.

The most complex to admit, as intemperate patients to the asylum, were those who were away from home, or with no regular abode. They were not always in their drunken state actually capable of wandering and Richard (197/4438) a cattle drover from Lutterworth was found lying in the fields and was taken to a workhouse prior to his asylum admission. Whereas, another Richard (203/6169) was found in a similar state by the local doctor in a wood near to Shepshed. Robert (205/121) from Melton Mowbray had been found totally naked in a private park. Admission of the intemperate often required the presence of police with handcuffs at the ready. A framework knitter from Loughborough must have had frequent rendezvous with the police as he was – 'locked up in prison between 20 & 30 times - says all the drugs in the world are imported direct to him.' (196/4277)

There does appear to be at times a less empathic attitude, towards patients who have self inflicted themselves, into the position of mental illness through serious abuse of alcohol. George (192/2979) a cigar maker from Brunswick Street Leicester, was quoted as being 'addicted to intemperance'. Arthur (192/3210) a sixteen-year-old shoemaker also from Leicester was 'addicted to the habit of self-pollution'. For William (185/616) a tailor from Northampton the consequence of excessive intemperance was that he 'wandered from pot house to pot house'. Joseph (187/1505) a wool carder from Leicester was defined as a 'hard drinker'. Lucy (187/1545) from Bingham in Nottinghamshire had latterly indulged herself in 'spirituous potations'. Another Joseph (197/4503) a marine store dealer from Hinckley, had had a serious problem with alcohol, for he had told the asylum doctor that 'he has never known what it was like to be sober for the last five years'. Charles (202/5894) a groom & gardener from Melton was quoted as suffering from 'acute alcoholic mania'. Dorcas (190/2480) had lived a very irregular life in London frequenting gin palaces & low eating-houses. Priscilla's (198/4920) husband from Ashby Magna had had to place her in a home for inebriates and a Sanatorium before she was eventually admitted to the Asylum. One female habitual drunkard (212/126) admitted in April 1908, had been sentenced March 23rd at the Borough Police Court, to spend 3 years in Brentby Inebriates Reformatory; she became very troublesome there & was then certified to be insane. Charles (201/5485) a bricklayer's labourer from Broomleys in Coalville was admitted at the young age of 18 suffering from simple mania with an assigned cause of intemperance. He was recorded as spending a good deal of his time in public houses and 'to have drunk considerably more than a youth of his age ought to have done'. On the Saturday night before admission in February 1894, 'he had spent 17 shillings and 6 pence treating himself and his friends to drinks'.

An individual's occupation was often not a direct advantage when trying to remain temperate. George (185/639) a maltster from Melton Mowbray had 'too many opportunities to be resisted of giving way to drink and thus eliciting the excitability to which he was constitutionally subject'. William (191/2806) a publican suffered from melancholia, perhaps as a direct consequence of him almost always having immediate contact with public houses. James (191/2693) a barman in a Lutterworth Legion Shop, also again had too many ready opportunities for indulgence in liquor.

Thomas (185/674) a boatman from Leicester had developed 'the constant habit of drinking, to keep out the cold in winter and relieve his thirst in the summer'. Stephen (192/2872) a grazier from Scraptoft had been accustomed 'to take a considerable amount of fermented liquors especially on Market days, but had not been a confirmed drinker'.

There were other reasons for actual work causing mental distress and accentuating intemperate habits. There was distress caused by a lack of trade: Or there was the success of good wages to spend. William (185/605) a watchmaker from Silver Street in Leicester, took to becoming intemperate during lapses in his trade. It was not always the type or location of job but the remuneration from partaking in it. Mary (187/1596) from Newton Burgoland ended up spending in a few hours, a month's wages on drink. Charles (191/2745) was a very skilful wool sorter and had taken large wages, which he unfortunately squandered, on all sorts of strong drinks. Excessive drinking, especially over prolonged periods has never benefited the health. John (185/617) a surgeon from Leicester had during his medical training in London, 'spent a very considerable sum of money in pursuits of the lowest description - years of indulgence in excessive drinking brought on inflammation of the brain'.

Alcohol did not always just damage an individual's health it also inflicted serious injury to their character. From June 1856 there was a section within the case books to define a patient's character. Sometimes the choice of data entry was directly related to an individual's relationship with alcohol. There were the 'goodies' thousands of them. The 'temperate' many hundreds of them, or 'abstainers,' the good as to 'sobriety', 'fairly temperate' & 'steady drinkers', 'the good', 'the steady', 'the sober' & 'respectable', 'the good sober' & 'the industrious', or 'the used to drink once'. Then there were the 'baddies' with a few hundred actually just classified as 'intemperate'; they had absolutely no other definition to their character. Others are recorded with such terms as 'hereditary intemperance', 'bad', 'intemperate', 'quarrelsome' or 'drinks plenty of beer'.

In the space for carry through information during a patients stay there is far more information on their previous loss of character through alcohol. Several had formerly been sober & hard working individuals. Many had very aggravated characters, which had been produced through a long course of intemperance. Domestic happiness was also often lost through a family member or members becoming intemperate. This was often not just because of drastic changes in normal behavioural patterns within households, but it was also due to family finances being under severe strain, owing to the neglect of previous business concerns. Joseph a carrier from South Kilworth was: -

> '... a case of maniacal exhaustion, the patient who a short time since was worth £79 kept a
> public house in Leicester and treated everyone who came his way, such was his liberality
> in this respect, that he speedily exhausted funds that might have served a better purpose ,
> and when misfortune and disease overtook him, he was friendless and penniless - this led
> to the affection of his mind.' (186/920)

Fortunately, a few patients were established teetotallers & two of them were named Fanny. The first (210/137) a fireman's wife from Shardlow had always been an inveterate tea drinker. The second (211-135) from Lyddington, even as a barmaid, had shown no signs of intemperance; in fact she was stated to have been almost a teetotaller. There is just one case mentioned where a patient had problems because he was a tee-totaller. William (206/61) a set maker from Enderby had gone up to work in a quarry in Northumberland: -

'... about 9 weeks before Xmas his bed fellow got delirium tremors during the night and half strangles the patient. Says that his late landlord had a grudge against him because he never drank - he (the landlord) thought there was something unnatural about teetotallers.'

Incidence of Suicides leading to Asylum admissions

Many regardless of the reason for their low mental health, just could not cope with any plans to soldier on in life. Performing intense accidents to the self, making serious attempts at suicide, was another reason to get an individual admitted as soon as possible.

'Suicidal cases exhibit great craft to carry out there unhappy desires'.[17] 9th September 1891

Several who attempted suicides were sent to prison before being admitted to the asylum, as was the case for John (201/5482) a blackmith's striker from Coalville. Ann (187/1384) from Narborough was like many others impelled to suicide & was placed in the Asylum as a precaution against it. Robert from Empingham had very definite intentions: -

'His propensity to suicide may be said to be constant his common salutation being "Have you brought me a knife or poison"' (187/1575)

There were several ways in which suicide was attempted before admission and these included - hanging, drowning, and the use of sharp instruments, poison, jumping from a height and throwing themselves under vehicles. Suicidal patients who chose drowning to end their lives, had generally been admitted after attempts & prior to becoming an asylum patient. Canals, rivers, water butts (211/42), buckets (211/88), ornamental water at a cemetery (187/1722), reservoirs, lakes (such as Groby Pool (195/3958)), water cisterns (200/5399), Shepshed sewer (205/118) and wells were also used. Phoebe (210/38) from Markfield must have travelled a considerable distance to throw herself into the Nuneaton Canal. Guy (204/32) a box maker from South Kilworth tried to drown himself, but the water was so cold he had had second thoughts. Marianne (186/1090) had thrown herself into a canal and continued on admission to be 'suffering from the effects of the immersion'. Martha (201/5488) from Mushroom Lane Woodville, wanted to drown herself and 'she had cried all day, because she could not get through the ice'. Sarah whose place of abode was recorded as Shropshire made a suicide attempt, which was recorded as follows: -

'She precipitated herself into a deep well, hoping thereby to shuffle off this mortal toil and thus save others from the evils she imagined she was inflicting, the shock to the nervous system she underwent, however, and a fond clinging to life, induced her to take a firm hold of the bucket at the bottom of the well, by which she was drawn up and safely reached terra firma.' (186/971)

Some mentally disturbed individuals were rescued from potentially tragic situations. John (187/1732) from Derby, who was discovered partially dressed by the canal side was, meditating on taking his own life. Jesse (200/5309) was found dragging a pond for his wife & children whom he said had drowned there. Frederick (199/5116) a civil engineer from Lutterworth had been recorded as recently

---

17 Superintendent's Journal DE3533-88

returning from India. He was noted as having had 2 attacks of sunstroke, one of them being quite recent in Nagpur. On his return home he had jumped overboard into the Red Sea, but was rescued & kept under surveillance for the rest of the return voyage.

Several patients entered the Asylum with self-inflicted throat wounds. Joseph (204/146) a coal miner from Atherstone had crossed the road to a butcher's slaughterhouse & declared he had to be killed. Avery (187/1630) from Woodgate Leicester had attempted to throw herself under carriages. William (206/5) from Redmile threw himself under a train, which resulted in him having to have his left arm amputated. Julia (201/5489) from Illston on the Hill threw herself into a sand pit. Both Catherine (186/1104 in 1850) from Leicester & Mary Ellen (210/136 in 1903) from Grantham both took large quantities of laudanum. Caroline (211/33 in 1904) who was admitted from Leicester General Infirmary, had swallowed quantities of an eye lotion containing atropine. Whilst Kate (210/127 in 1903) from Loughborough, had swallowed some hair lotion, 3 weeks before her admission & had been taken to Loughborough Hospital. Sarah (193/3231 in 1871) from Coleorton took a large draft of paraffin for the purpose of putting an end to her existence. A lady named Hilda (212/9 in 1906) from Queninborough tried to poison herself by taking large doses of Friars Balsam. Mary Elizabeth (212/110) from Market Bosworth not only threw herself into the swill tub (managing to get out of it herself) she 'also drank a Bottle of Fluid Horse Blister.' Mary (194/3662) from Market Bosworth had swallowed a two-shilling piece, thinking that it would kill her. Henry had taken a quantity of white lead. (203/6085 in 1876). A lady from Bagworth (212/122 in 1908) had tried to poison herself by drinking the contents of a Leclanché cell battery.

Some patients exhibited far more basic & less horrendous ways of endangering their lives. Hannah (201/5436) from Ravenstone's general health had not been good for about 2 years from whence she had either refused food or not taken it regularly and this appears to have been the prime reason for her admission. Jane (185/584) from Loughborough is quoted as suffering from 'anorexia' in January 1845. Even if the principle intention had not been to actually take their own lives Sarah Ann (211/122) a cook from Lutterworth 'Had knocked herself about was taken to the Cottage Hospital where she had to be tied down.' & Lucy from Somerby (211/132) had also performed considerable degrees of self harm,'knocked her head with a rolling pin & flat iron, repeatedly bruised her face with her fist.'

Some of the suicidal may have felt that they were actually supporting their families by doing away with their lives. Frances (212/18) a machinist from Enderby had threatened to drown herself & cut her head off, in order for her to be out of the way.

The Patients Delusions & Illusions

There were the suicidal and then there were those patients who were exceptionally far from themselves, within the asylum complex. Numerous patients were diagnosed as suffering from various forms of delusion or illusion. Many patients felt quite safe within those same delusions. Were the delusions or illusions just part of a dream that a mentally ill person had believed to be an actual event? John from Oadby: -

> 'He has enlisted and deserted three times in the Royal Scots Guard & in a Lancashire Regiment. At home frequently men dressed up as women used to come into his room at night.' (199/5036)

At times it must have been difficult for the asylum staff to know whether information they were receiving was a truth or a delusion. Richard a railway platelayer from Great Bowden records say: -

> 'He seemed confused and spoke about shadows blue & yellow which came about when he closed his eyes. It is noticed that when spoken to about these, he closes his eyes and presses upon them, and perhaps this accounts for the delusion, for anybody can see shadows if they press upon their eyes.' (205/131)

A lady from Leire told the doctors that; 'She has lived 20 years in Tasmania or Van Diemon's Land'. (195/3965) Sarah (187/1549) from Ratby perhaps had more significant local knowledge of innovations within the national rail system than the asylum medical staff themselves. In October 1854 she declared that there was a system of underground Railway communicating with the village of Ratby. This was not a major delusion within her thought waves. There is still in fact an old underground rail track (now blocked up) running from Glenfield which was at the time the first station from Leicester West Bridge on the Leicester & Swannington Railway, (leading then on in the open air to Ratby station), which was opened on 17th July 1832 as the world's third steam railway. Just before reaching the station the line passed through Glenfield Tunnel, which at 1 mile 36 yards long was at the time the world's longest railway tunnel and was built by Robert Stephenson. John a fire brigade superintendent from Ashby may also have been quite forward thinking, when he informed the staff in October 1897: -

> 'Has involved a scheme for defending England by digging trenches all around the coast.' (197/4478)

On Sarah's (186/1153) certificate of admission it stated that the supposed cause of her mania was fright from espying a rat & that she still had visions of them. It is hoped that this was in fact an illusion. Several of the delusions were incredible over exaggerations. Henry (192/3038) believed himself to be over four hundred years old. Edward a senile labourer admitted from Grantham Workhouse: -

> 'Said he was a good singer and insisted on singing "Christians Awake". Says he has swallowed a hansom cab and two good horses & that he knows people who have swallowed omnibuses.' (205/72)

John (205/119) a farm labourer from Atherstone, admitted suffering from mental ill health, induced by intemperance, believed his wife who was over 70 had been carrying on with the Baptist Minister & she was consequentially 'in the family way'. Mary (189/2022) from St Martins, fancied that she had had a living child within her for 10 years. A labourer from Kibworth was very confident in his physical abilities: -

> 'He says he is training to fight with Bendigo, also that his father had been a great prize fighter.' (194/3510)

William a coachman from Gopsall Hall, admitted in November 1906: -

> 'Says the world came to an end 25 years ago - & that this is a new world. Says he has travelled all over England & America & that he has got nearest to the North Pole of all the explorers.' (206/38)

Henry a young game keeper (admitted in April 1904) whose assigned cause of illness was questionably given as adolescence was recorded: -

> 'Says he has been to Australia to play cricket - Says he can shoot a sparrow at a 1000 miles.' (205/53)

Many of these fantasies were dependant on patients having acquired considerable knowledge of the big wide world around them. James (190/2465) a tin man & brazier admitted in August 1863 – 'Was present at the burning of Moscow, twelve years previously, and had seen Napoleon 1st there'. In 1900, Ann (203/6140) from Windmill Hill in Woodhouse Eaves, who worshipped at the Church of England –

> 'Was going to Rome to blow up the Pope with dynamite'.

John a knitter from Barrack Yard in Burbage, who was admitted on 11th October 1886, had the cause as onset for his condition, written as 'Excitement from hearing of the earthquakes and the end of the world.' His records also say: -

> 'He states that the world is shortly coming to an end & that the Black tribes are coming to turn out its present inhabitants.' (197/4708)

A sausage casing maker who lived in Syston had an idea of going to America to buy sausage skins: -

> 'He says he is going to America that the passage will take 4 months - that the sea will be kept smooth for him - as he is the Prince of Wales.' (217CCB/221)

Elizabeth (211/73) from Grantham was incessantly seeing insects crawling on the walls. A lady from Frolesworth named Harriett (212/87) had some quite vivid visual delusions, 'Sees elephants & tigers in the sky upside down.' A seamer from Grove Street (189/2924) was having problems with a beloved son enlisting in the army and she was – 'full of many absurd delusions such as fancying that chairs and tables are moving about the room.' Many had exalted ideas about their relations with royalty (such as an Ann 211/5). The individuals themselves were totally convinced that they were for example various high-ranking personalities or well-known figures such as Queen Victoria (198/4885-203/6140), a Pharaoh (186/1261) or Jack the Ripper (199/5041-199/5118). A man named Henry (194/3719) was married to the Shah of Persia's daughter. In 1907 Archie (206/67) from Great Bowden had met Winston Churchill dressed as a tramp & had invited him in for tea. Certain patients were so within another identity that they expected to be addressed in line with their delusional beliefs and would not be pleased if they were referred to by their name on the case book admission documentation.

The delusions were not necessarily totally self-orientated. Many had delusions about their immediate family or contacts rather than their actual selves. Several patients believed that they had close contacts with Prince Albert (192/2861-194/3658-192/2943) and that he was actually arranging a couple of patients' discharge. A man admitted from Lancaster Street in Leicester, believed that he was able to assist in achieving any patient's freedom: -

> 'Declared himself as Custodian of the Asylum & possessed the Open sesame key.' (217CCB/185)

There were some quite traumatic illusions such as believing that dead children were still alive and must be taken out of their graves. Samuel (194/3733) had quite a load to carry, as a Mr Walker was actually constantly sitting on his shoulder.

Martha a lady from Leicester had delusions about having a far more exciting profession than her own, which was charring: -

> Patient is under the delusion that she is a private detective that she has rendered great services to the nation which ought to be very grateful to her: she said she received a certificate from her late majesty Queen Victoria just before the Boer War commenced - she came to Leicester began to talk wildly & attracted the attention of the police.' (212/8)

William from Wigston had continuous and various extreme illusions: -

> 'He declared that he was the Crown Prince of Europe - Is stated that he had an accident to head some years ago in coal pit - has exulted ideas says his real name is "Albert Edward Nolan Nelson Gladstone Immanuel says he was invited over to Germany by the Emperor - but he preferred his own freedom - 53 years ago he was the Crown Prince of Europe- but it is not the title but the heart of the man that makes the difference. Says all his money to the tune of 57 millions is in the hands of the government in the national debt - & that he is only having the interest at present about 17 millions - Says he is the Prince of Wales & presented Victoria Park to Leicester - Calls himself Prince Rupert Albert - Says he owns the Midlands Railway & is General Director-Chief Inspector - Says he is Albert Edward Beaumatite & he is a visitor looking after the management of the Asylum health, - Tells me he is commander-in-chief-of the Bristol Forces that all his sons are generals in the British Army - Told me he had to stay here to manage the place and that everything was carried out according to his instructions - Chief of the principal armies in the world'. (205/16)

Within the identity of someone else, many found themselves incredibly wealthy. John (190/2546) a scissor grinder had become the owner of Buckingham Palace and had 600 ships filled with gold. Samuel (197/4624) from Newtown Linford had become the owner of the Bradgate Estate. Charles (206/147) from Blaby spoke of his fortune '£200,000,000'. Joseph (192/2977) fancied he had 7 coal pits and 6 silver mines besides having £10,000 at York. Henry (205/50) had six trains, full of furniture for all his houses.

Patients also had delusions relating to immediate families or near neighbours. Mary (210/35) a general stoker's wife from Ibstock, fancied she could hear her daughter's children crying in distant Yorkshire. Mary Ann (211/97) from Hinckley was convinced that her previously deceased parents were still alive and locked up in a dungeon somewhere. Ellen (210/78) had problems with the neighbours coming down her chimney & calling her foul names. Henry (197/4612) from Aylestone believed his neighbours were putting gunpowder down his chimney. Sarah Hannah (210/101) from Markfield would frequently shout down a well near to her house. Elderly Annie (210/40) from Easthorpe believed that there was a subterranean tunnel running to her house from Mr Sibson's cottage over the road. The passageway had been made in an attempt to try to stink her out. The same Annie also had to cope with the illusion that a local farm hand had brought a ladder for a thief who had stolen her pictures of Baden Powell & Kitchener. In the bake house near to Hannah at Thringstone, she deluded that very strange things were taking place: -

> 'She says that at a bake house near her house they throw men & women into the ovens & send them out as bread to feed people in hell.' (212/92)

It was at times problematical trying to persuade patients to go out into the airing courts for some fresh air. Frederick (217CCB/285) in 1887 was not keen to use them, 'as he didn't like mixing with the other fellows as they were all Russians.' Many had more technical illusions, which may have been inspired by the new, up and coming innovative technologies. Elizabeth (212/25) from Loughborough believed that there was some form of direct communication between her bedroom & the local railway station. The new energy electricity influenced many of those with weaker mental patterns. The records for Mary Ann from Bardon Hill, admitted in April 1895 reveal: -

'She says she has been undermined by the sciences which work upon her in the shape of electricity.' (201/5598)

Harriet (200/5385) from Loughborough believed that boys carrying boxes could give you shocks without the intervention of wires. Mary Ann (191/2782) from Friar Lane, Leicester (admitted in November 1867) had apparently been reading books on electricity & actually wrongly believed her daughter had been electrified. Jane from Easthorpe believed that: -

'She could not light the kitchen fire, as there were people who drew the fire up by electricity & who would consequentially set the chimney on fire. The same electricity destroyed her piano. She had difficulty sleeping at night due to the smell of electricity & she also complained of an inhuman law, which allows people to torment them with electric needle.' (210/39)

Mary from Uppingham was for a time quite 'cock-a-hoop' with her thoughts in 1893: -

'She had been annoyed by means of "electric gas" from next door - that six German men & six German Women of bad repute frequently insulted her - she recently wrote a letter addressed the Head of Scotland Yard saying she was the daughter of a Lady of title and was deprived of her possessions and then gave a description of herself (a rather flattering one).' (201/5419)

David (193/3105) from Scalford fancied himself in March 1870 as a piece of machinery and wanted a blacksmith to put him back in working order. Eleanor (202/5853), in June 1897 spoke of having had visions and said that the Almighty had photographed her. Ann (195/3947) talked about people using window machines whereby they looked at her & talked to her, to her constant annoyance. A domestic servant named Alice (198/4930) had in February 1899, many illusions about telegraphs and telephones. A lady admitted in September 1907, whose former address was found to be Stannington, Sheffield had been found wandering in Leicester and nothing was known about her but she told the officers preparing her certificate for admission that: -

'States she has been worked at wireless telegraphy, but would sooner cut her limbs off than state where she worked for Marconi.' (212/89)

Traditional folklore & customs most have had the potential to nurture or even initiate certain delusions or illusions. Elizabeth (210/105) a domestic servant from Ashby de la Zouch stated how afraid she was of being slaughtered & 'that she crossed her knives & forks & that the leaves in the cup meant her chap was running after her.'

Some of the illusions must have needed an incredible degree of healing to ease them away. Martha (186/1197) originally from a Union Workhouse was under the hallucination that she had been murdered one and a half years ago. A young female draper's assistant from Snibston who had a year previously been operated on a tumour of her intestines at the Leicester Royal Infirmary, believed that she had been buried before breakfast. (212/12) Another former, elderly, Barrow on Soar, workhouse inmate named Hannah (212/21) was really frightened by her delusion, as she had delusions that the workhouse was on fire and that she and the other inmates were going to be burnt to death. George (204/28) from Whitwick, was continually talking to himself and imaginary people from unknown countries down drain pipes. Ann (188P46/VOL3/1141) was continually engaged in washing imaginary clothes. Joseph a gardener from Derbyshire, was in October 1893, exceptionally well before his time, as a hallucinating recycler: -

'Says he is 'Lord of all the Earth', all the wheat & the gold being his, also the potatoes. Says he can covert all the rubbish in the airing courts into most useful things'. (197/4418)

Josiah (205/61) from Husbands Bosworth was visited in August 1904 by an angel, who sat on the windowsill informing him that the end of the world was coming and that he himself would die within 3 days, because his throat was so bad. He actually died of a malignant condition of the oesophagus, and the angel on the windowsill appears to have picked up the serious condition way before any doctors from the asylum had. Joseph (201/5547) a collier from Ashby refused to stand still, for he was frightened that if he did so he would be shot where he stood.

Many patients did recover and were able to discuss their delusions as actual delusions. Individuals such as Henry (205/148) from Birstall who at one time declared himself as king and that he was due to open parliament, later on when nearly recovered, if the staff mentioned the opening of parliament to him he declared: - 'We will let bygones be bygones'. Ann (197/4696) from Newtown Linford also recovered from her delusions of having been once possessed with immense wealth, laughing & declared, 'It's ah humbug'.

The North West quadrangle of the Asylum, which would have been used as an airing court for female clients. 1920's photograph, courtesy of University of Leicester Archives.

Problematic behaviours both outside & inside the Asylum following admission

The mentally handicapped & the elderly who were no longer blessed with their normal brain capacity, could not be expected to always exhibit tolerant behaviours. The mentally ill, who had perhaps no congenital or senile handicap, were also capable due to their illness of exhibiting extremely deviant and dangerous behavioural patterns. Behaviours ranged from socially problematic to extremely dangerous and they were quite a challenge when the staff were trying to maintain a safe environment within the asylum. Some of those behaviours were actually criminal & many retained their criminal tendencies as a patient within the asylum walls. One man tried to sell three of the asylum hats in his ward and after not getting a suitable offer he destroyed them (197/4517). Another patient would pick pockets for the tobacco of others who were watching theatrical performances and then try to sell it to other patients the next day (199/5107). One elderly gentleman was admitted as a criminal inmate; he did eventually recover but had to remain in under a Secondary States warrant (185/626). Three patients John (187/1622), Peter (193/3201) & David (193/3105) were also ultimately considered to be well enough to be sent back to gaol.

The number of attendants was flexible, according to the numbers of patients and generally the intentions were, that there should be one attendant for 25 inmates, who did not exhibit problematic behaviours and one attendant for every 15 patients who were more violent or dangerous & needing more help with personal cleanliness. The following table has been compiled from the Salaries Register & is calculated on a quarterly basis the numbers of staff divided into keepers, nurses, outdoor or indoor patients for each quarter[18]: -

Date	Keepers	Nurses	Outdoor Servant	Indoor servants
31/3/1849	7	8	5	3
30/6/1849	9	11	7	4
30/9/1849	12	13	5	4
31/12/1849	11	14	6	4
30/3/1850	13	12	5	4
30/6/1850	11	13	5	4
30/9/1850	9	12	5	4
29/12/1850	11	12	8	4
29/3/1851	11	12	5	5
20/6/1851	12	14	5	4
27/9/1851	13	13	6	5
27/12/1851	11	17	8	4
27/3/1852	11	13	7	4

18   Asylum Register of Salaries & Wages DE3533-94

Several patients did cause serious staffing difficulties. To take one example, Robert (195/3918) a railway fireman from Wigston, had to be removed to Ward 2, after having refused all compliance with the discipline of the asylum. Another Elizabeth (196/4114) was 'unwilling to fall in with the rules and discipline of the institution.' The attendants and nurses within the asylum had enough to do, without also having to cope with these challenging behaviours. Lucy (197/4564) from Great Bowden was recorded as taking one persons entire time, to prevent her from doing mischief. It took at least three nurses to dress Margaret (197/4664) from Caldecote and she would snatch at any watch chain if she got a chance. Whereas Mary (190/2475) from Thringstone needed the assiduous attention of two nurses, wherever she was. This Mary's actions must have had drastic effects on the staffing ratio at the time. Sarah (191/2748) from Railway Terrace in Loughborough likewise required the constant attention of a nurse both day & night for as she made many different violent attempts at suicide. Some of the patients when in a state of great excitement would need six or eight attendants to overpower them. Initially, Hilda (211/143) a twenty year old idiot, must have caused considerable physical difficulties for staff, as she had to be carried everywhere. It would often take several nurses or attendants to bathe & dress patients. There was an Elizabeth (186/1101) recorded whose habits were exceedingly dirty; she refused to change her linen and slept in her ordinary clothes and 'was quite incapable of conducting the ordinary affairs of life' Attendants' clothes could be completely destroyed and individuals, both staff & patients, were knocked about in all directions.

Some of the behavioural problems were quite minor and it was generally just a case of slightly annoying other patients. Ann (190/2359) from Whetstone was constantly crying out 'What a shame'. Elizabeth (212/52) from Britannia Yard, Hinckley 'would groan for hours'. Rebecca (197/4575) from Whitwell was found to be 'beyond managing to be very quiet'. Young John from Ashby cannot have been the best company as 'he would rock himself to & fro & shriek like an engine.' (193/3347) William (202/5901) a blacksmith from Markfield would continually reiterate, 'God the Father, God the Son & God the Holy Ghost'. Some would cause considerable irritation to those around by continually reading aloud or singing all day long. Anna Maria (198/4800) once a nurse from Market Harborough had a mission to turn on as many taps as she could. There were also the socially unacceptable habits of 'pulling noses' (203/6131), 'continually running from corner to corner' 192/2948), or 'sprinting down the gallery' (196/4342), continually 'spitting', or 'snatching the food from others at meal times'. A melancholic wheelwright from Market Overton (217CCB/89) was apparently never contented, if indoors he wanted to be out & if outdoors he wanted to be in. Bertie (204/92) from Uppingham annoyed old people by pulling their chairs away from them, just as they were about to sit down. Various things would be disarranged in the ward and one patient classified as an idiot, even got into the coal-hole and filled her mouth & bosom with coal (189/1981). One patient from Great Bowden ended up absolutely covered in feathers after he had torn open a feather bed and got inside it (194/3538). Harriet (197/4621) from Waltham actually threw the contents of her chamber pot over her neighbour. There were those who were continually opening windows, whereas others would be constantly closing them. If individuals were feeling like Mary Ann from Leicester, then it is no wonder that windows were adjusted: -

> 'She has peculiar sensations, she gets burning hot, so that she has to run out of the house or open all the doors & windows, she feels if she did not get out she would die.' (212/20)

Some patients usually those that were very ill were placed in single rooms and Walter (202/5878) a young imbecile aged 7 from Rugby would continually pop in and out of these rooms and if he found shelves he would clamber up them.

The greatest irritation would come from those patients who would be a problem both night and day. Dorothy (193/3337) from Burbage was, '..perpetually moving, seldom remaining for more than a few seconds in the same posture…she seldom sleeps'. A lady from Syston named Isabella (212/50) had quite unusual difficulties at night – 'She tells me at night that she has to seek for her insides which have got lost somewhere in the bed.' Harriet (191/2750) a schoolmistress from Hinckley would frequently not go to bed at all at night time. Julia (211/17) from Sapcote actually had to be held down in bed. Another Harriett (200/5208) who had had disappointments in love, rarely slept but at least she would lay quietly awake. One patient Ann (196/4352) rarely if ever seemed to sleep, but her strength never appeared to fail her. Elizabeth (203/6132) from Edith Weston would be a real nuisance by encouraging other patients to get out of their beds. The elderly Sophia (191/2735) would get up in the night insisting that it was daytime and she became quite violent if threatened. John (195/4098) from Loughborough would consequentially get very cold by continually getting out of his bed. Frederick (205/145) a pipe maker from Leicester would be constantly throwing off his bedclothes. Samuel (194/3480) from Leicester had a passion for destroying things but the ' things' were usually other patients' blankets and 'the special flannel shirt that had been provided at his own request never suffered any damage'. Daniel (196/4229) from Quorndon became so very restless at night, continually getting out of his bed, that he was ordered to sleep in the epileptic dormitory. One attendant was required to sleep in or near every dormitory and each dormitory was either to have a light burning all night or a means of immediately obtaining a light.

Many patients' activities would go far beyond just being rather troublesome or a general nuisance. When it came to attacking others or self-mutilation, this was a far more serious problem. One patient knocked himself on the head with an earthenware chamber pot. Agnes (194/3633) from Bringhurst seemed to be absolutely regardless of pain and 'would pick up live coals from the fire' or touch the exceedingly 'hot doors of the American asylum stoves', which had been especially imported from America in 1874. If knives could be procured, especially whilst doing various asylum occupations such as potato knives, then the suicidal would make sad use of them. William (196/4117) from Diseworth was 'found to have a foreign body in his throat'. An oesophageal tube was used to extract the whole lining of a hat. Lionel from Brooke was not so fortunate on 29th March 1884 as he died 9 days later: -

> 'While in the airing court this afternoon swallowed a stone – which he describes as being about the size of a walnut – he did not at first make any complaint but at tea he brought back all that he had swallowed. Had to be operated on as all attempts to extract it failed.' (193/3162)

Inmates would also at times attack others. .– Edward (188/1753) was recorded as '…knocking himself and others about in all directions.' – Eliza (197/4408) was '..inclined to offer violence to anyone within her reach.' Careful supervision was necessary to obviate various melancholic events or catastrophes. There were times when able bodied patients such as Henry (196/4338) from Barrow's assistance was immediately appropriate, when he helped an attendant who was being struck by another patient.

William (202/5886) a builder's labourer from Ratby, 'declared his readiness to fight any man and he did not care how big he was'. Backs were jumped on, ribs were broken and lens in eyes were dislocated. Black eyes were sadly often abundant within the asylum walls and William (199/5046) from Hinckley would 'try to lighten his frequent black eyes with chalk'.

Some of the badly chosen behaviours became somewhat indecent. Boots would be urinated in and patients would undress themselves at inappropriate hours. The actual cause of Thomas from Kensington's mania, who was born in 1814, was recorded as being 'intense study & masturbation': -

> 'Maniacal excitement preceded by much mental anxiety the consequence of intense study and an indulgence to a certain propensity at the early age of sixteen. The history of this patient is rather chequered, at the age of sixteen he was a brilliant scholar, spoke several languages, was a Poet, a Draughtsman and a mathematician, he also paints, is a musician and an astronomer, he has lived in France and Rome and speaks the dead and living languages, he has been confined in Bethlehem Hospital in Peckham House and at Kensington and has been insane more or less for eighteen years ...This patient underwent a long course of medical treatment with considerable benefit, but whenever improvement manifested itself, and he felt at all equal to exertion, he began to play his old tricks trying every scheme in his power to effect his escape, which he has done from every Asylum where he has been confined - he succeeded in the present instance by removing part of the window frame of his dormitory, and letting himself down by means of his bed clothes.' (186/900)

Samuel from Kegworth was not as intelligent as Thomas from Kensington, but he manifested similar problems in 1856.

> 'He practices masturbation in a most shameless manner.' (187/1724)

Boots would be urinated in and patients would undress themselves at inappropriate hours. Mary (190/4066) a drover's wife, who was very far from her home in Buckminster, would bathe her face in the closet water. John from Birstall, whilst being mentally ill, committed several indecent acts and one of them was, 'Making water into the mug he was drinking from and drinking from it again.' (189/1974) One male patient when placed in the padded room 'plastered the walls with excrement'. (202/5901)

It was far more likely for the staff to be the ones who were attacked. Joseph (187/1484) from Blackfordby who had been the subject of constant self-abuse in one fit of excitement, which may have been epileptically driven, succeeded in a savage assault, to completely destroy his attendant's clothes. Rebecca (190/2417) another patient from Blackfordby caused considerable damage to Nurse Platts 'breaking both her arms, 2 fingers and making 20 wounds to her scalp'. John (191/2802) certainly new what he was about with his challenging behaviour – 'Tried to injure the attendant by kicking at his privates.' A basin of beef tea got thrown over one attendant. Whilst another attendant suffered superficial wounds after being hit on the head with a chamber pot held by Henry (191/2797). In the case of Richard (189/2204) from Burbage it is difficult to interpret, who was attacking who: -

'Has a black eye was given to him by his attendant Bacon. Richard having attempted to overcome Bacon. Bacon was engaged in the struggle with another patient & Richard having left his place at the breakfast table for the purpose of aiding T…. the patient engaged in fighting Bacon'.

During these attacks asylum property was at times damaged. There were the window smashers. Elizabeth (187/1483) from Oakham was the champion window smasher, as in one week in May 1855; she managed to break 50 panes of glass. Richard (188/1863) from Sutton Cheney must have also broken a few windows as he attempted to thrust furniture through them. Emma (192/3002) admitted in 1869 from Liverpool, had broken several panes of glass, in her attempt to escape to get married. A boot once broke one of the paintings in the day room (191/2793). Harriet (196/4225) from Loughborough managed 'to stop all the house drains with prayer books, pocket-handkerchiefs & sunbonnets'. Another patient who had developed a taste for destruction was very partial 'to stuffing anything he could find down the water closets' (188/1863). For another inmate it was his torn clothes that had the same destination. If clothes were not torn then it would be the rugs that suffered the same fate. Also all the plants in the ward were once pulled to bits. One man originally from London had records that say: -

'He was very destructive to bushes and plants in front garden some time ago & requires to be kept in the Airing Court.' (217CCB/37)

In September 1883 and in August 1884 two hospital feline friends were denied their right to have two lives, let alone nine (196/4272-197/4500).

If you definitely did not want to go out into the airing court then a positive move would be to undress oneself. Patient safety was of prime importance and any wound, however it was received, appeared to be always entered in the case notes. Charles (196/4342) & Ann (196/4288) both tried to set a room on fire. And Ann (196/4288) from Kirby Mallory exhibited more perilous behaviours – 'by locking herself in a bedroom and setting fire to a bundle of rags'. Catherine (193/3219) from Belgrave nearly strangled the child of another patient, because she believed that other patients were trying to make out that it was her child.

Restraints were at times used to ease demands on the staff. Several patients had to be placed in special strong clothes so that they could not tear them to bits. Women had to wear 'ticking dresses' which appear to be more indestructible. Some of the dresses had such toughened fabric & strong stitching that it was believed that they could probably have withstood a 'force - ten gale'. Fanny (196/4330) from Loughborough though could tear these 'strong dresses' with little if any difficulty. Mary (197/4577) from Loughborough would also tear portions of her dresses but would declare that 'it was of no consequence, as she would mend them again'. In consequence of Robert (195/3761) from Barrow persistent destructiveness to clothes, he was obliged to be dressed in a strong canvas suit. Jonathan (192/2955) from Barwell would tear off his clothes as soon as they were put on. John (185/763) from Quorndon, rarely let a day pass without some act of violence, either to others or himself and special gloves were required to prevent him tearing at his own flesh. On 3rd June 1878 Selina was required to use canvas gloves occasionally too on some days, to prevent her picking her face into large sores, which she often did.[19] Sarah (217/159) from Anstey, also required canvas gloves

---

19 Leicestershire & Rutland County Medical Journals LRO DE3533-277

day and night & had a long sleeved ticking dress 27/6/1878. John (196/4271) was so constantly taking his boots off that he had to be given a pair of 'locking' boots. A groom from Loughborough would constantly try to put two boots on the same foot (197/4689). Henry (196/4135) from Oakham was not allowed laces for his boots, as he would break them up into small pieces. Samuel (197/4636) from Thurcaston would post his bootlaces through any keyhole he could find. William (206/15) from Market Harborough was so restless & untidy that it was necessary to have his jacket buttoned at the back so as to stop him constantly undressing himself. William (202/5901) the blacksmith from Markfield caused 'so much damage to furniture by kicking out, that he had to have both his arms and legs bound'. 'Stout', 'short' or 'straight' waistcoats were not only used to facilitate admission they were also occasionally, but not frequently used, whilst patients were actual patients. Two records within the medical journals mention a Thomas requiring a straight waistcoat for 12 hours due to maniacal delusions; violence & suicidal acts and Joseph had to have his hands attached to a waist belt for 12 hours due to surgical reasons.[20]

With certain patients 'special measures' had to be resorted to if safety was to prevail. Those with a strong propensity to suicide had to be watched both day and night. Some like Sarah (197/4415) from Loughborough who when being taken for a picnic by train actually tried to jump in front of the train were actually given a precautionary red ticket, at the asylum. Frederick (197/4659) from Bitteswell attempted to strangle himself with his pocket-handkerchief in 1886. After this particular incident it appears that the clothes of the patients were locked up at night and given out in the morning again. The last place that the well-behaved patients would be was on Ward 2, or the refractory ward, and it was the location for patients who had refused all compliance with discipline. In 1847 Thomas (185/786) from Lutterworth is recorded as having to have 'a night watch'. Some patients had to be placed in guarded rooms or padded rooms. William (187/1636) from Dadlington actually managed to destroy the padding in a padded room. At times certain punishments were given to discourage bad behaviour or habits. Elijah (196/4134) from Shepshed had 'undergone a suitable punishment of a shower bath for 20 seconds'. In two medical journals[21] there are four columns for Patients who are, or since the last Entry have been, under Restraint or in Seclusion, when and for what period, and reasons, and in the cases of Restraint by what means. Between 8th September 1873 & 4th April 1887 (these are the only records surviving) there are 32 cases recorded of patients being required to be placed in seclusion. It was not just the 'Charity' patients who received some form punishment for unacceptable behaviour, the 'private' patients were expected to conform too & they received exactly the same penalty to try to ensure a modification in their challenging behaviour. After Mary (201/5447) from Kegworth had been extremely annoying by calling other patients foul names and as she continued to be 'not choice' she was put in 'a room' for half an hour. There are absolutely no details on the room and if in fact it was actually a 'padded room'. A certain Mary was put in 'the room' 14 times. The main reason for the need for seclusion was maniacal excitement, violence & destruction. The length of time of seclusion very noticeably dropped in a space of 3 years, from more normally 6 to 8 hours to Mary 45 minutes for smashing breakfast things & Charlotte 30 minutes for 5 times pulling things off the table whilst dinner was being served.[22]

---

20   Leicestershire & Rutland County Medical Journals LRO DE3533-277

21   Leicestershire & Rutland County Medical Journals LRO DE3533-277-278

22   Leicestershire & Rutland County Medical Journals LRO DE3533-278

The staff must at times have perhaps wished that the exceptionally badly behaved could have been elsewhere. The elsewhere they would have perhaps thought of would though definitely not have been 'the great escape'. The staff were expected to maintain the status of a patient, as a patient, and not as a free member of the great outside world, until they had officially recovered or were sufficiently relieved. Patients who escaped, were liable to cause formidable problems and one of those problems, was the hole such attempts made, in asylum finances. It was not always easy retrieving an absconder & if the police had to be involved then the cost could be quite prohibitive as was the case in January 1856 when the recapture of a couple of patients was recorded as costing £2.16.6d.[23] Not all patients could be held within the safety of the asylum, as several longed to be on the other side of the walls, usually to decamp to be back with their families. The family would usually be the first place where they were found, as was the case of Joshua (193/3351) the labourer who first went home to Thurlaston & then to Birmingham to his brother. The most ardent escapers who would have a go 'at every favourable opportunity' & often had to be placed in guarded rooms. In May 1880 Mary from Wymondham managed to escape by the window of her room a ten bedded room and was found almost naked on the Railway by a signal man … 'she suffered no particular inconvenience from her dreadful midnight avocation'.[24] Henry (196/4346) from Burton Lazars was one new entrant who was absolutely not going to stay. On the first night, when the night watchman opened his bedroom door about ten hours after admission Henry knocked him down and locked him in the room. He did exactly the same again on the following evening. Mary (195/4066) the drover's wife from Buckminster was also determined to escape & 'squeezed through a window rather under 6 inches opening'. If one was determined to get out, then exceptionally inclement weather, preferably dense fog, should be taken full advantage of. Edward (206/35) formerly a clerk was working in the gardens and successfully made his get away in such weather and during alterations necessitating the patients to go outdoors in thick fog, a wall also was successfully scaled by Thomas (194/3560).

A prime item to secure an exit without any fog was to have a key. On one occasion several patients managed to procure a key by overcoming an attendant. George (199/5191) who had been a soldier for many years in India and could understand Hindustani had arrived at the asylum intemperate and could not get rid of his strong craving for drink. He found an old disused key, with which he let himself out and was found half drunk in an inn nearby. If you could not procure a key, then you made your own from a piece of wire, as William (188/1768) did and so as not to be missed, he arranged his clothes to resemble a figure lying in bed. Many escape attempts without any keys involved successful ascents. One patient named Hannah (187/1539) after being left without any proper supervision made use of the scaffolding in the new airing ground to escape. William (190/2463) tried to contrive his escape by getting on other patients shoulders and leaping over the wall in the exercise yard & Matthew (196/4202) successfully attempted to scale the airing court wall. Benjamin (192/2961) from Wymeswold attempted a valiant escape by trying to get up a chimney. One lady made a really dangerous escape, by escaping through a trap door on to the roof. Windows were broken and window frames were very carefully loosened to activate freedom.

---

23 Superintendent's Journal DE3533-185-675

24 Superintendent's Journal DE3533-86

The asylum philosophy was not to keep the patients locked up, but to where ever possible give its inmates experiences of a more normal lifestyle. One of the activities was to take a walk outside the Asylum grounds; several patients partaking in this form of leisure took advantage of the opportunity to be home again. Sometimes groups of patients made up a form of walking party, Walter (202/5816) from Hugglescote, made his get away from one of these. Michael (195/3756) originally a Dubliner was allowed out to the Roman Catholic Chapel, to practise his religion, but he never returned from his third trip out. John (200/5247) a publican from Great Bowden was allowed out with one of the other patients named William (200/5291) on 28th September 1893, to see a foundation stone being laid for the chapel in Clarendon Park but he absconded to Rugby. The same William who shared the stone laying ceremony later got into a tradesman's cart and drove towards the front gate.

Many escaped whilst performing their recuperative occupations whilst a patient. The most common avenue of escape was via the outside work on the Newtown Unthank farm. Thomas (193/3346) from Atherstone hid himself in the straw stack at the end of the day. Peter (193/3201) chose not to hide and managed to run a considerable distance from the farm, but he was speedily recaptured. Escapes from the farm working party could be relatively easy but were also facilitated by intense fog. John (197/4754) from Medbourne ran away from the vegetable house: Joseph from Sileby absconded from the potato house. Whilst William (200/5318) from Huncote was carrying clothes to the laundry, he suddenly bolted getting over the iron railings and ran across the racecourse to Victoria Park. Mary (191/2624) from Shepshed when she worked in the laundry ran away and was brought back by the coal cart man. Frank (205/88) had been employed in the bake house and was sent to work one Sunday morning at 6.30 am to set up the ovens, but an hour and a half later he was logged as missing. He sadly died soon afterwards, whilst in a coma, produced by alcoholism and exposure.

Several attempts were also made to escape from the cricket matches. One cricket match escapee was on the list for being under ardent watchful eyes, because of his continuous evident intentions to escape. Herbert (206/58) from Market Harborough was once thought to have escaped but was found lying quite sick in bed. William (198/4925) a framework knitter from Huncote made a successful 'great escape', lasting longer than the statutory period of 14 days and was therefore discharged from the asylum.

The police were continually used to retrieve patients who had escaped the Asylum. There were also sometimes problems with patients who had been allowed home on leave, who either escaped from or caused problems within their 'leave' environment. Henry (191/2690) from Quorndon had to be brought back as he had become violent and Thomas (192/3075) got very drunk & was found lying in the road having an epileptic fit.

Normally, all these problematic behaviours were more problematic for the adults in charge. There were a few cases noted though where the behaviours even though they were far from normal, were essentially by their obsessive nature, only perhaps a problem for the patient themselves. John (204/126) a retired librarian from Tinwell who became a patient in March 1903, admitted that he continually washed his chessmen everyday & could not give a satisfactory reason for such proceedings. The teenage Alfred (205/45) from Oadby had a dozen books, which he would enjoy placing very methodically upon a table. He would grunt with delight when the arrangement was complete. Edward (197/4589) from Whissendine (admitted as a patient in September 1885) would wash himself four or fives times more than usual in a day. Sarah Ann (211-100) from Lutterworth became highly excitable and would continually change her clothing. Ann (217CCB/225) was 'continually putting on buttoning & unbuttoning her garments'. A coachman (205/39) from Burton on the Wolds, whose head five years previously, had been injured by a horses hoof was, 'Constantly packing and unpacking his things'.

There were not only problematic behaviours with the patients sometimes the actions of staff caused major difficulties too. The problems were no doubt exacerbated by most of the staff actually having to be resident within the asylum walls, as part of their employment contract. To be given board & lodging could though have made the jobs quite sought after, but wages were never very high. Wages are entered on a quarterly basis within the Salaries & Wages Register.[25] For the quarter ending 29th March 1851, the salaries were as follows - The Superintendent £75 - The Asylum Matron £13/2/6d -

The Asylum Chaplain £10 - The Asylum Clerk £35.12.6d. The 11 keepers & 12 nurses wages for a quarter were approximately £4 each for a quarter. The indoor & outdoor workers including the gardener received a wage of approximately £3.5 shillings for a quarter.

To be on the wages register, the staff were expected to uphold certain principles. The Asylum regulations were made very clear to the staff regardless of their status: -

'Confinement, probation or punishment of any inmate' was forbidden without medical authority. There was to be 'no deceit or terrifying of patients, or irritation by mockery or mimicry'. The keepers 'shall not indulge or express vindictive feelings'; they were to 'forgive all petulance on the part of the patients and treat with equal tenderness those who give the least trouble'." [26]

Photograph of Asylum Matron.
Stewart Collection courtesy of ROLLR.

---

25   Salaries & Wages March 1849-Dec 1862 DE3533-94

26   Asylum Regulations 1837, Rules 1849 & 1894

The superintendent did not only have the behaviours of those within the asylum walls he also had to contend with events outside that were in no way directly related to the running of the asylum itself, as was the case in August 1867: -

> 'I desire to draw your notice to the fact that a large beer house has recently been erected upon a small field near the Wigston Toll Gate and that by means of extensively used advertisements, fireworks, & bands & music large numbers of noisy people are collected therefore out doors dancing, causing much disturbance to the patients.'[27]

One of the negative inclusions within the Superintendent's Journals relating to asylum staff was on 17th February 1870 when Theodosia a laundry maid & Robert an attendant were both suspended from further service as a consequence of Theodosia being absent from the laundry a great proportion of the night on two nights. A nurse named Sarah also suffered the same fate, as she could not give a satisfactory account of certain articles belonging to a certain patient who had recently died. A tea cloth marked M" was found at the residence of an attendant Joseph. On 11th May 1870 a 2nd Class nurse named Ann had to be suspended in consequence of her being pregnant. In November 1875 Daniel a 2nd class attendant was suspended for having used unnecessary violence to a pauper patient. When two nurses were found to have given a problematic patient several blows to the face the Superintendent held an enquiry & censure was passed upon both nurses. The Official Visitors who also kept a regular inspective check on the asylum and its running had to report on Burton a porter who had been found drunk after a Harvest Festival one evening and he had also been severely reprimanded some two months before, for being drunk at Newtown Unthank Farm during the official visit of the House Committee.[28]

Whatever the failings were with any member of staff, to be fair, any recorded examples of staff misdemeanours within the Superintendent's Journals, were very few & far between.

Photo of Dr Rothsay C. Stewart one of the former Medical Superintendent's from 1895 until the time of the asylum's closure in 1908. Stewart Collection courtesy of ROLLR.

---

27   Superintendent's Journal DE3533-84

28   Asylum House Visitors Book DE3533-9A

Photograph of Superintendent's Office. Stewart Collection courtesy of ROLLR.

Photograph of Superintendent's Office. Stewart Collection courtesy of ROLLR.

Photographs of Patients.
Asylum Casebooks courtesy of ROLLR.

Treatment within 'The House of Cure'

'A house of cure and not a house of detention'.[29] This initial aim on the opening of the asylum in 10th May 1837 never lost its focus, even when the accommodation for 'curable cases' became limited due to space being taken up by potentially no longer curable cases. The Superintendents & his staff always withheld their positive attitude even though a number of patients were unable to do the same: -

> 'Says it was no good her taking food or doing anything - that she would never be any better.' Annie from Sileby (212/19)

The superintendent viewed, the lack of available placements as a 'yearly increasing evil' that he needed to draw people's attention to. In the following inclusion in a case book, he is referring to John (185/675) from Ashby Folville: -

> 'Upon referring to the date of admission and the recent date of the patient's illness it will be seen how rapid the recovery was and how important it is to subject insanity to adequate treatment in its early stage.'

Every patient, even the frailest of the frail were still treated with positive attitudes. . Some recovered in weeks: Some took years to recover like Ann (186/1035) a servant from Portsmouth whose 'recovery tho' slow was perfect and satisfactory.' A steady slow recovery may have been fine for certain patients but for an asylum, which was at times too full for comfort, it was very far from fitting. Several like Suzannah (186/939) from Birstall had to be discharged earlier than usual on account of the crowded state of the house. The Superintendent was often seriously hampered by the want of room for new admissions with the offices holding numerous applications for more serious cases.

What were the consequences of all the good intentions and efforts within the 'House of Cure'? So many positive things continually happened within the Leicestershire & Rutland Lunatic Asylum: Less positive things were inevitably happening too. The reclassification of patients to a more serious complaint, usually with the adjective 'chronic' was one of the negative sides of detailed record keeping. Another far from positive event was a patient's death within the asylum.

Many patients at the time of admission were tragically, quite critically ill. Annie (212/35) an imbecile, aged just 18 from Coleorton, who was also suffering from epilepsy, arrived at 12.35 pm 29th August 1906, died at 9.35 pm on the same day. A hosiery hand from Loughborough was admitted & her initial medical report closed with the words – 'Looks as if she is suffering from an acute disease & is very ill.' This unfortunate lady died of pneumonia just 8 days later. The statistics for patients who died relatively soon after admission (not including those classified as idiots & imbeciles & those admitted aged 61 or over) truly emphasize the high numbers of patients who were seriously ill at the time of entry. At least eight patients died on the day of admission or the very next day. George (194/3680) had severely slashed his throat at Market Harborough Union House the night before the day of his demise at the asylum. At least 259 died within a month of admission & almost 700 died within a year of admission and another virtual 700 died within the first five years as a patient.

---

29   Leicestershire & Rutland Lunatic Asylum. Rules for the General Management of the Institution with Prefactory Remarks by the Committee of Visitors I.S. Crossley Leicester 1849

The doctors usually appear to have been immediately called, especially if death was unexpectedly on its way - 'just in time to see his last breathe' (191/2592) - 'was immediately in attendance and 'found her at her last gasp' (191/2623).

Mary Jane (212/40) from Ratcliffe Road, Loughborough had been operated on for cancer of the uterus just prior to admission – the suspected cause of her mental condition is given as 'cancer' – she died 3 months later, of the same condition in the asylum. Some of the cancer sufferers were more fortunate. A Sarah Ellen (212/12) from Snibston had been admitted after having had surgery for a tumour of the intestines, she leaves the asylum completely recovered several months later in March 1907. Susan a farmer's wife from Markfield had been operated on for ascites in 1846. When the water collected again she was traumatically disappointed and died two weeks following her asylum admission. (185/768) The figures for the results of treatments show that approximately a third of all admissions actually died in the asylum.

Within these statistics are though high numbers of individuals being admitted in old age, those suffering from serious epilepsy, heart disease, chest complaints, or some form of paralysis. Over three hundred patients have the word 'paralysis' either included within the brief diagnosis of their medical state on admission, or as part of the reason for their death. At times just the word 'paralysis' is used in isolation from any other medical detail. Twenty-six patients died from paralysis. The youngest to die from paralysis was Thomas (191/2744) a 26 year old sailor from Tugby. The eldest was Jarvis (187/1317) a retired butcher from Syston who died at the age of 77. At other times 'paralysis' is used in conjunction with other diseases of the brain such as 'cerebral softening', tumours or epilepsy. A far more likely addition to the term 'paralysis' is the adjective 'general'. If a patient is defined, as suffering from 'general paralysis' then it appears that they had also contracted syphilis usually by physical contact with another sufferer or much more rarely through hereditary sources. John (185/763) from Quorndon, could have been a patient afflicted with a hereditary form of this paralysis, as he was admitted at the age of 15, having been a sufferer of an unspecified mental defect for 5 years & dies 4 years later with his cause of death being 'general paralysis.' The later stages of syphilis usually led to some form of serious mental derangement & William (189/2126) a labourer from South Luffenham is noted within a Case Book as, 'Rapidly approaching the last stage of general paralysis'. Annie (212/14) from Hugglescote was unable stand & on admission had to be carried into the ward, eleven days later she died with the cause of death being given as 'syphilis'. Two hundred and ten patients have 'general paralysis' given as their cause of death, 44 of them were women and 166 were men. Sometimes 'General Paralysis of the Insane' is entered in the abbreviated form of 'GPI'. The stigma from contracting a venereal disease could lead to a sufferer understandably experiencing considerable humiliation. William (187/1385) a grazier from Billesdon has the cause of his suffering to be - 'Despondency produced by pecuniary losses and embarrassment from general paralysis'. James (186/1201) a framework knitter from Leicester was afflicted by both general paralysis & slumps within the hosiery industry. Maria (186/983) a shoe binder from Leicester actually has the cause of her death in April 1851, given as 'paralysie des alienes'.

There were also the extreme medical problems of epidemics. There are several inclusions of patients having been infected with 'tussis' (pertussis whooping cough) within the records. In 1858 smallpox made its appearance in No 4 Ward. There were various attacks of profound infections such as phthisis and influenza. At least a dozen patients suffered a severe bout of influenza, three with this form of infection were actually admitted with sub-acute mania - Mary (199/5174) died within 3 days and Ann (199/5176) with Martha (200/5336) in a couple of weeks. In 1891, 8 of the male staff and 7 of the female staff together with twenty or more patients were recorded in the journal as having been attacked by virulent influenza.

> 'Great inconvenience has ensued in carrying on the work, as the diminished staff had not only the sick patients to attend to but their sick fellow-servants as well – on the whole we have managed very well, although all the kitchen servants were ill at one time & the baker succumbed two days ago & had to go home. The cooking has been carried on very well indeed by AM Jno Smith who was 20 years in the Army & used to cook for his mess at times'. [30]

> 'There has been a great amount of sickness & absence from duty on the part of the Male attendants no less than 5 being away from the Asylum at one time. I propose to issue an order that attendants absent from the asylum on the grounds of sickness, should forfeit their pay during such an absence'. [31]

A Millicent (196/4377) was admitted with an assigned cause of illness as scarlet fever, twelve days later she was dead. Minnie (210/36) had exhibited a strange manner since suffering scarlet fever at the age of 15. She improved a little, & after a time she went in to service, but was not a success & up to the present year 1901 (when Minnie was aged 19), she has been in 32 situations. Frederick (202/5861) with melancholia, Robert (193/3383) with chronic mania & Annie (200/5374) with simple mania, all had the assigned cause of their illness as phthisis. There were well over 200 patients who appeared to enter with only mental illness & who would later die at the asylum due to phthisis, consumption or tuberculosis sometimes together with other medical conditions. A proportion of the two hundred who contracted these then terminal diseases of the lungs could well have contracted the condition in the asylum itself. The earliest death from phthisis at the asylum was Mary (185/655) a framework knitter from Great Wigston who died 6th November 1851. Deaths from the condition carried on right through up until the asylum's actual closure. Sixteen patients died of consumption and 23 patients died from tuberculosis and only one of these 39 patients (Thomas 186/1262 a framework knitter) appear to have more definitely contracted the infection, outside the asylum before his admission. One of the attendants was recorded as being absent from his post owing to severe phthisis. Whenever influenza struck then it was given written acclamation in the Medical Superintendent's Journals as a worrying problem which should be recorded, but high incidence of phthisis seemed to have an attitude of - there is nothing we can do about it given towards it. Phthisis was though quite commonly included within the hereditary details for any patient. It was not just whether a blood relative had mental illness: It was also whether any close relative had some form of lung disease. Emily (211/117) from Earl Shilton had 'two sisters who were consumptive.' For some the family duties of caring for relatives with phthisis had been the potential cause of an individual's insanity. A laundress (210/144) working at Ayston had to go home in the evenings to 'look after her phthisised sister'. It was believed that her mental instability was the result of the strain, caused by working both day & night. Annie (211/118) from Quorndon's mother had died from phthisis.

---

30 Superintendents Journal DE3533-88

31 Superintendents Journal DE3533-85

Other than often being the follow up mention to hereditary mental illness, within the case notes, these infectious conditions of the lungs appear to be almost taken for granted by the record keepers.

There were also eight patients who died from typhoid fever, but several of that group appear to have actually entered the asylum, probably mentally disrupted by the condition. Several patients had not contracted typhoid themselves but they were grief stricken through the loss of close relatives, who had been infected with typhoid. One patient died seven weeks after admission having been infected with English cholera in Blaby in May 1847 (185/801). In March 1875 during an outbreak of erysipelas a very efficient young Nurse named Julia Smith in No 4 Ward volunteered to take charge of the patients with erysipelas in a temporary fever house. At times of epidemic it was deemed necessary to restrict visiting sessions.

Other clinical complaints, which led to death in the asylum, were apoplexy, bowel problems, cancer, dropsy, gangrene and renal complaints. Some more rare reasons for death were appendicitis, ascites, carbuncle, cellulitus, choking or diabetes. One of the most tragic deaths must have been the case of John (195/3778) a young 7-year-old idiot: -

> 'I regret I have to report a deplorable accident which occurred to a patient an epileptic & idiotic child on the 25th May. This patient John William aged 7 was admitted about 2 years ago from Thorpe Satchville and on the day mentioned fell while in a fit into the fire place of his ward by which means his clothes caught fire and he received considerable but superficial burns thereby, and he died on the following day of shock to the nervous system'.[32] 9th June 1880

For many the emotional tensions had led to certain patients, not coping with themselves: They just had to get away. Unfortunately, the only way they could envisage this happening, was to take their own lives. A significant number of suicidal patients were admitted to keep them safe and only eight such patients appear to be actually successful in committing suicide within the asylum itself during almost seventy years of treating patients. A strip of sheet (186/1305), a towel (194/3656) & a pocket-handkerchief (187/1434) all aided the loss of life through strangulation. A knitting needle (205/146), and a quantity of white lead (203/6085) were less successful. A marine James (193/3330) from Sparrow Hill in Loughborough, would tear his clothes to make chords which he would then tighten around his neck. William (185/705) cut his throat whilst working in the shrubberies and Sarah (196/4212) from Timber Hill Melton Mowbray who had murdered her husband a well sinker with a knife, before she became a patient, managed to cut her own throat with a knife twenty eight days after her admission. Thomas (194/3627) from Ilston had made fatal use of a scythe on the Newtown Unthank Asylum farm. William (185/705) from Leicester who had been attacked with brain fever, whilst being in the West Indies for 11 years, had found it too hot whilst mangling in the laundry, but after requesting to work in the gardens, he retired to the shrubberies & 'destroyed himself 'by cutting his throat. At times it was not the tools but the commodities involved. These suicidal incidents within the Asylum usually led to detailed information of the events, being reported within columns of the local newspapers and cuttings of which have been kept within the patient's Case Book Records. Another more purely mental condition, which led to over a hundred patients death, was 'maniacal excitement' or 'melancholic exhaustion'.

---

32 Superintendent's Journal DE3533-86

Many of these deaths in the asylum were to some extent an inevitable consequence of virtually untreatable clinical conditions. The patients were admitted to be, where possible, made well again, or at least enough relieved from their mental problems, to be fit to return to society. The medical men were not going to sit back & watch their patients needlessly deteriorate. Their continual positive approaches were often not helped by certain patients 'joie de vivre'! Jane (202/5798) a widowed knitter is recorded as 'wandering about with a face as long as a ladder.' Henry (187/1722) who had attempted to drown himself at the cemetery ornamental waters, when returning from chapel (187/1722) was 'unamused, glum, silent & unassociating.'

One of the patients' first avenues of aid was to ensure the very basic needs of man, which was appropriate & sufficient food. Ensuring that both patients & staff had reasonable meals was just one more task for the current Superintendent to take charge of. The Official Visitors came to check on many things and one of those items was the food. They not only looked, they actually tasted it: -

> 'Dinner which was much improved and which all appeared to enjoy. Dinner consisted of soup, Bread & Plumb pudding'.[33]

To help cater for the food provisions, the asylum grew its own crops at the Asylum Farm at Newtown Unthank, but extremes of weather often played havoc with these crops. Problems with the potato crop had to lead to temporary alterations in dietary needs. In October 1857, 12 ounces of boiled rice, was ready to be substituted for the one pound of potatoes normally in use. In 1868, all varieties of potatoes including early, middle and lates were not up to their usual standards. In July 1904, a severe drought hit the sacred potato crop & the asylum was forced to buy potatoes. There were the ups too with the asylum farm potato planting. As in August 1878 approximately 400 bushels of Early Rose Potatoes were raised. After carefully removing the bad ones the potatoes were carefully placed in clamps. On 14th June 1882, The Superintendent's Journal records the Asylum-Garden & land being cultivated as follows. There were 10 acres of potatoes chiefly Early Rose, Myatts, Magnums, Champions or Ash Leaf. Two acres were used to cultivate beans both Kidney & Broad, plus an acre and a half for peas. There were about 5 acres of cabbages together with broccoli, kale & cauliflowers. Another two and a half acres were used for Mangolds & Swedes. A few acres were remaining for small crops such as carrots, turnips, onions, parsnips & fruits. There were finally 7 acres of meadow or grassland. The farm was so successful, that at times, they actually managed to run it effecting considerable profit for the asylum funding. In 1881 there are records of the customary sales of fruit & vegetables by auction on Saturday mornings. In October 1883, the same records list the stock on the farm as 30 sheep with 13 lambs, 10 theaves, 6 ewes with 1 ram and finally 84 pigs including 9 sows & 1 boar. Eight bacon pigs had just been successfully sold for £53.10d. The asylum was at times essentially, quite a very self-supporting community.

If man was actually going to manage to live on bread alone, then it would certainly not be on the asylum bread of July 1857. The bread supplied to the Asylum, during the preceding quarter by a certain baker, had been of 'very objectionable character' whilst another baker's bread had been in contrast of a 'uniformly good' description. The difficulty in getting good quality bread was probably one of the reasons why they eventually built a baker's shop and made their own loaves. In February

---

33   Asylum House Visitors Book 20th January 1893 DE3533-9A

1883 when a new bake house was being built, arrangements had to be made to contract for the supply of bread with a baker in the city for 3 or 4 weeks, so as to allow the new oven to become seasoned after being built. Problems were not over with the quality of bread even when they baked their own, for eventually the major component of bread, the flour contracted in to bake the bread, was at times of inferior quality. By August 1903, bread baskets had been placed on the tables during dinner times and the patients were able to help themselves to what they required. One of the great successes in the supply of provisions was in May 1882, when the milk supplied from the Newtown Farm, was very good & was much appreciated by the Inmates – It is recorded 'as containing 10 per cent of cream according to the use of a graduated glass'[34]. Unfortunately, this situation did not last for in December 1891 there was a problem with the asylum's milk which although quite sweet on a few days, it presented quite a peculiar appearance. The Superintendent obviously cared enough for his patients & staff to at times call in the experts. In 1875 when an experienced cheese buyer tasted the cheese, it was felt to be not good enough. The asylum had their own cellars to keep the cheese in. The tea was also tested by the official visitors on their regular visits & on October 21st 1891 it was found to be 'quite equal to sample'. [35]

In June 1869 the superintendent wanting to ensure nutritious diets for both patients and staff started a trial of preserved meats from abroad: -

> 'I have as an experiment sanctioned a trial of Australian meat and as a result of last Wednesdays experiment, I am anxious to have your permission to purchase sufficient quantity of it for a supply for the whole asylum once a week – during the summer months. The meat is well flavoured – and has the appearance of being well fed. Today the dinner consists of preserved mutton.'[36]

> 'I desire to draw your attention to some new preparations of tinned meat – Compressed corned beef from Chicago taking it will be useful as an article of diet for use in this asylum. 13th Sept 1876 …the Chicago Pressed Beef has been used on three occasions & appears to be much liked by the patients'. [37]

In August 1867 the asylum had difficulties in procuring beef supplies because of the exceptionally hot weather.

> 'I have been constrained to substituting a dinner of bacon once a week – a change which has been very acceptable to the patients.'[38]

In the 1880's meat provisions were often quite unsatisfactory-'coarse & inferior kind – hard & tough'. Not only was the meat substandard in November 1875 it was also 5lbs short of the actual weight that had been paid for. In July 1883 there were reports of some meat being returned as unfit for use.

---

34   Superintendents Journal DE3533-85

35   Asylum House Visitors Book DE3533-9A

36   Superintendents Journal DE3533-84

37   Superintendents Journal DE3533-85

38   Superintendents Journal DE3533-84

There was then an incredible amount of pre-planning that went into one of the most strategic times of the asylum day, the meal times. To ensure adequate diets were actually happening, diet sheets were even displayed in the main hall for the public & other visitors to see. The asylum was catering for many incoming patients that had been used to undergoing horrendous privations in food. Eliza a seamer from Leicester was one such incoming patient: -

'…for some weeks prior to her admission she had been unable to procure the commonest needs of life & had been up to the Asylum gates to buy a meal!!' (187/1560)

A young four-year-old idiot named Arthur (195/3757) from Hugglescote had been accustomed to live solely on bread before admission and after a more nutritious diet at the asylum, including beef tea, 'he soon gained colour to his previous milk white cheeks'. Rachel (196/4150) a busy mother from Oakham wanted to make sure that her husband who had a great appetite always had sufficient to eat and by doing so deprived herself of enough to eat. The dietary provision at the asylum appears to have been successful as John (197/4403) a groom from Muston gained 3 stones in weight following his admission & and William (193/3097) an imbecile from Loughborough at one weight check had gained 18 pounds since his admission.

Not everybody was well enough to be able to partake of a normal daily diet. Joshua (193/3351) from Thurlaston appears to be one of the earliest vegetarians, as he never ate any meat. The very fragile would often only take portions of the specially prepared beef tea. Jane (185/736) from Leicester was ordered a liberal & nutritious diet 'without any vegetables'. An elderly widower James (201/555), who had been admitted from Lutterworth Union, was only able to take liquids and had lived on brandy & milk since his admission. Thomas (186/893) from Ashby was ordered meat everyday, bread, port wine, linseed tea & he also was to have no vegetables. Margaret (191/2791) from Glen Parva continued to have half a pint of brandy every week. A very frail, elderly, beer house keeper from Barrow was allowed ½ pint of milk daily. (188/1736)

There were certain patients who had what was termed 'a disinclination to food' & just would not eat. Rebecca (195/3942) of Great Glen 'believed herself to be dead inside so that there was no point in eating'. Agnes (210/1) from Woodville believed that the food stayed in her chest and could not pass into her bowels & that she was much better when her stomach was empty. She sadly died eight days later; her cause of death is recorded as 'exhaustion from refusal of food'. Elizabeth (189/2216) & William (194/3442) were both not keen eaters & continually had to be dragged to the table. Lucy (186/923) from Leicester had for many weeks refused all sustenance. A Great Bowden villager Mary (201/5438) 'would not take a morsel'. Hannah (201/5436) from Ravenstone was admitted because she was not eating. With great determination & perseverance the attendants would try to persuade William (191/2605) from Oadby 'to take anything at all in the shape of food'. John (193/3122) an agent from Leicester also continually refused his food, with great obstinacy. Daniel (196/4209) a tailor from Barrowden would only take his food if he were fed like a child. Sarah from Hathern also had a history of a problematic dietary pattern: -

'Before she had influenza, she was quite a stout woman, but since has wasted rapidly. She was fed twice with the oesophageal tube but owing to her state of extreme prostration this method of administering sustention was obliged to be discontinued - she was then fed solely by the feeder & teaspoon with eggs, beef tea, milk and brandy in small quantities at short intervals, but she tried not to take anything & would scarcely swallow at all'. (200/5351)

Frank (203/6087) a framework knitter from Loughborough was very obstinate in taking his food and preferred apparently to put it in his pocket & eat it when he was unobserved. Lucy (211/83) a former workhouse patient had wrapped food in her bedclothes to prevent the devil from taking it. Fanny (203/6070) from Loughborough had to be urged to take her food, as she believed that there were 'spirits' in it who talked to her & told her things that she did not like to hear. She would though not tell the staff what the 'spirits' told her. Some patients were rather particular about what they ate for a variety of reasons. John (205/135) a licensed hawker from Loughborough would not eat pork or bacon because he believed the bible prohibited him from doing so. Another John (206/70) from Shepshed reported that he often saw a powder on the surface of his tea & cocoa. A framework knitter from Loughborough fancied that the staff were trying to poison him and would make them taste everything before he would take anything (204/14). Mary (187/1477) a gentlewoman from Belgrave Gate, imagined that any article of diet, which she may have been induced to swallow, might suffocate her. Some of the abstainers, like Hannah (189/2211) from Ashby, had to be fed by means of a stomach pump and it appears that those who had difficulty eating were fed via an oesophageal tube. Sarah (201/5601) from Derby took egg & milk by means of a soft elastic nose tube. Richard (191/2781) a roadman from Groby was unable to swallow anything but a liquid diet, which had to be poured straight into his mouth. John (204/104) a quarry labourer from Mountsorrel who had suffered a horrendous fall before admission was fed by means of a feeding cup. Mary (195/3762) a seamer from Hinckley Union was also recorded as having to be fed with a feeding bottle. William (197/4712) a lime burner from Barrow, could only have slop or a milled diet. A labourer Michael (192/2853) who had an Irish accent was also prescribed milled dinners. It seemed that a couple of patients might have used, the action of not partaking of food as a route to taking their own life (188/1805).

In complete contrast to those who had difficulty eating were those with ravenous hungers. Ann (196/4286) from Barkby was recorded as not appearing to have any mind, but instead had an immense appetite. George (205/23) a clergyman from Cosby, was frequently moaning about the long intervals between meals. Whereas William (196/4116) from Cranoe complained that he had nothing to eat since being brought to the asylum. A domestic servant from Ashby named Emma (193/3318) complained that she was being starved & that the food was insufficient. Peter (187/1392) an imbecile from Leicester Union had an absolutely voracious appetite and he bolted his food without any mastication at all. Ann (187/1366) from Leicester also had an enormous appetite amounting to 'bulimia'. A housewife from Bottesford had an absolute passion for potatoes and had to be watched during meal times, as 'she would bolt off with them from the plates of others'. (196/4266) A farm labourer from Melton (195/4027) would ramble about after meals crawling under tables, picking up & eating all the crumbs.

Meal times at the asylum were then not always trouble free. Certain patients often required more than one nurse to feed them. It would of course be both frustrating & worrying for an inmate to vomit up food that had taken so long for some member of staff to feed them. John (187/1720) had the habit of frequently vomiting his food with peculiar vehemence. At times the food and the vessel would take flight across a room, often in the direction of a member of staff. A few patients who refused to take the necessary medicine would have to have it added to their food. A notable number of patients also arrived being noted with deranged or temporarily blocked digestive systems. For incoming patients initial priority was given to their digestive systems & constipated bowels if that was their condition. There were a surprising number recorded with this problem. John a carpenter & joiner admitted in 1847 and recovered within 4 months, had the following inclusion: -

'It was found that his bowels had for a length of time been much confined and the injections brought away an immense mass of hardened and dark coloured faeces and as soon as this source of inconvenience was removed he rapidly recovered his health & reason, took his food as other men and eventually left the Institution quite recovered.' (185/798)

One of the doctor's chief medications for the very frail was the same alcohol that they so despised for blackening the character & lives of many other incoming patients. At the same time that they found liquors abhorrent for their detrimental effect on health, they also realised the curative role that it could play. Ale or wine was preferred as part of a treatment plan to the more intoxicating liquors. The Superintendent or House Surgeon would specifically order alcohol for inmates if they believed that it could offer medicinal benefit.

Some of the patients were exceptionally frail at the time of admission and were in desperate need of an immediate pick me up. Elizabeth (185/759) from Quorndon was one patient who for a length of time had been in a most precarious state and for many days it had been extremely doubtful if she would survive. Her naturally strong constitution together with wine, brandy, warmth and quiet at length brought her round, but it was apparently many weeks before she regained her health and strength.

Many far less fragile patients were actually ordered pints of ale daily. John (187/1488) the maltster from Preston in Rutland, quite understandably took very freely some extra allowance of ale every day. Elizabeth (191/2777) from Leicester had had wine every day since her admission. Mary (191/2779) from Loughborough had at one time been having an extra half pint of ale daily, but eventually this was no longer considered necessary. William (191/2806) a publican from Leicester had initially needed a supplement of brandy but later had half a pint of ale instead. There was also the aforementioned Comfort (185/804) from Husbands Bosworth whose quantity of consumption of brandy was reckoned to be 'at least a gallon'.

Eventually it was decided that cuts were to be made in the provision of alcohol

'As regards the beer given to the Patients - this ration of half a pint of beer for dinner has by permission been discontinued for about 100 of each sex – viz; to Idiots, Imbeciles, Dements & Epileptics. The results have been favourable on the whole and, except in one or two instances among the females, there have been no complaints whatsoever – The time of trial has been very short so far, but we think the wards have been quieter & that there have been less quarrels and confusion – and there has been a great saving in beer carrying from the kitchen to the various wards'.[39]

Those whose mental health was notably affected or caused by excessive input of alcohol, generally were either cured or died only a small percentage were long term patients, relocated or readmitted. The cause for readmission was usually patients reverting to their previous intemperate habits. Many though were able to go back to their previous jobs, on the other side of the asylum gates, like the wool sorter and the tollgate keeper. Mary (once an alcoholic from Leicester 186/981) could have lapsed into readmission within the space of twenty-four hours, for on the very evening of her

39 Superintendents Journal DE3533-89

discharge she was met by the nurse who had had the care of her, and eventually after the celebration of her release, 'she was conducted home in a state of beastly intoxication'. The superintendent was not amused.

Alongside the cures of a reasonable diet & curative portions of alcohol came the prescriptive potions or medicines. The extent of the use of prescriptive potions & drugs cannot fail to remind us that the asylum was a hospital, 'A House of Cure'. Amongst the entries in the case books were - banana water, peppermint water, lime water, gentian & tincture of rhubarb, castor oil, senna, salts, linseed oil, syrup of squills, hydrocyamic acid, the different preparations of quinine, iron confect, Sarsaparilla, morphine, Iceland moss, nitrate of silver, pediluvioum, night drafts or sedatives, blue pill, tartrate of potato, bromide, mustard plasters or cataplasms, opium & starch injections & anodyne draft to name just some of them. Much later on in 1902, Sarah Jane (210/89) from Wigston Magna, is recorded as requiring 'sedatives often.' Initially any medications were in the case books, but eventually specific Prescription Books are referred to within the case book records but they do not appear to have survived.[40] Photographic scans made from the early case book records emphasize the deep relationships between potential cure & various medications of the age within the Asylum.[41]

There were also amongst other treatments, particularly during the early years the 'blistening & purging'. Another treatment in the years soon after the opening of the asylum was the use of leeches. Leeches became so popular as a form of remedy, for various bodily conditions, that eventually shiploads had to be imported from Australia to meet the needs of the medical men.[42] Joseph (185/799) from Whitwick was 'repeatedly leeched, blistened and purged'. Another Joseph (185/678) from Newbold Verdon in March 1846,'..to have 8 leeches applied to the temples - to have 6 leeches applied behind the ears - and cold applications to the head'. An imbecile Robert: - 'Has had creosote & glycerine applied to his head for the last three weeks apparently with benefit as his hair is much thicker in consequence.' (191/2837) Thomas from Ashby in August 1848: -

> 'Ordered meat everyday, no vegetables, bread and port wine - linseed tea - twelve
> leeches to the abdomen and a mustard plaster to his chest.' (186/893)

The following patient, William (199/5009) a former soldier appeared to have been a virtual hypochondriac, for he was very fond of medicine and when in the army, he would often spend his spare cash on buying medicine. Once he had left the armed forces he did not rest satisfied unless he had some ailment that could be drugged. Maria (211/121) from Tugby also became 'hypochondricised - wrote out long lists of her complaints to her doctor'. In 1856 Warren a carpenter from Leicester: -

> 'About 12 years ago he went to consult the famous Wing woman who was a quack living
> in the county. The infusion of herbs, which she gave him, made him much worse -
> brought in from Camberwell Asylum.' (191/2820)

---

40   Asylum Patient Case Books DE3533-(186/949)(193/3096)

41   See Scans Pages 103.

42   Australian Geographic No 14 April-June 1989 Leech Mania Graeme Sims

Photographs of medications for certain patients taken from Case Book Entries.
Courtesy of ROLLR.

One framework knitter from Wymeswold had been treated for inflammation by the 'antipholgistic method' in 1849. (186/984) Thomas (197/4556) the foreman of the Midland Goods Depot from Great Bowden had a remarkable view of how his medicine worked,' Talks wildly says that my medicine goes in at his mouth and out of his great toe in less than 10 minutes'.

Another component tobacco was also mentioned in helping to relieve manias or melancholia. It was recorded just like alcohol, as a cause of the condition for some or a remedy for others. A gamekeeper from Croft: -

> A most inordinate love of tobacco the consequences were inevitable & for some months was the worst patient in the house - he acquired a degree of confidence to which he had long been as strange (185/631).

For Walter from Melton, tobacco appears to be feared as the cause of his low mental condition: -

> 'He seems to have periodic attacks of sullenness which often follow smoking - whether the smoking causes them we cannot determine but he has been ordered to be kept from smoking as an experiment." (217CCB/231)

A clergyman from Dunton Bassett was one of several patients noted 'to have smoked tobacco to an inordinate extent'[43]. George (185/794) a labourer from Leicester in 1847 who suffered very severe epileptic mania & in his case the use of tobacco by means of smoking was viewed as very beneficial.

There was then the good diet, the alcohol portions, the medicines & the leeches, which played a major part within the curative structure of 'The House of Cure & Not a House of Detention'. There was though another exceptionally strategic part of the cure & this was how the patient was able to spend his time within the asylum. A vital part of recovery will have included, a troubled mind having other things to think about, which were not directly related to their immediate problems. This was particularly important for those whose who were not fit enough for their free time to be spent actually working for the asylum, in some way, such in the laundry or out at Newbold Unthank on the Asylum farm.

A major part of the asylum day was though the hours spent asleep. By night it was hoped that the patients would get a reasonable nights slumber. Several patients like Richard (189/2213) a carrier from Leicester was given, 'Large doses of scotch ale, brandy and laudanum are freely given him but no sleep was obtained - Beyond large amount of scotch ale & slight dose of opium, no particular treatment was enjoined'. The asylum daylight hours would be spent either in or out. For the chronically ill the day would probably be spent indoors in bed. At the very best though, no patient would if possible be denied the opportunity to go outside,

> 'For the older & feebler women a Bath-chair was employed. No one has abused this great access of liberty so far – we are all amazed here at what we have been able to do in the way of innovations'.[44] 13th June 1883.

---

43   Asylum Case Books Records DE3533 (185/861) (195/4085) (185/795) (186/1232) (185/834)

44   Superintendent's Journal DE3533-86

Cure was not going to be achieved lying in bed or sitting around all day, when energy was available, patients were encouraged to be out and about and make use of that same energy. A framework knitter in 1857 became so physically incapacitated, that physiotherapy in the form of walking exercises were arranged for him (188/1787). Hannah (187/1414) in March 1854 was supplied with elastic stockings for her varicose veins. A prime route to cure was for a patient to be as purposefully active as possible. One of the very basic opportunities for fresh air was the 'airing ground' or 'airing court', or the 'exercise yard' - one for males & another for females.

Often several patients must have been out at the same time in these open-air areas, as when Richard (192/2913) went into the court he would molest anyone near him. In 1868 Esther (191/2833) was in trouble for injuring the flowers in the court. There were swings within this area as Elizabeth (193/3240) from Ashby Magna was very fond of swinging on them. On 12th October 1875 Jane received a blow in the mouth from a swinging boat, which resulted in 'one tooth being knocked out & her lips were contused & lacerated.'[45] The location of this swinging boat was not stated. In September 1884 the large male Airing-Court had to be covered with fine granite chippings & the coarse gravel pebbles were removed as they had so frequently been swallowed by patients – and on one occasion fatally (193/3162). Walking out from the 'locked in areas' of the asylum was viewed as a major part of recovery. The special paths constructed close to the asylum, were not any old basic pathways, (some around the garden were actually edged with tiles) and they were called 'promenades'. Later on some walks were edged with five hundred damaged sleepers. Trails not only went round the asylum, there were also excursions of various walking parties to neighbouring villages or the more accessible portions of the Leicester Forest.

'Many patients have been out walking beyond the asylum grounds, when the weather permits – Of the males only 51 patients are constantly confined to wards and airing courts; all the others viz at this date some 184 have liberty beyond the airing court at work or exercise or amusements or chapel. Of the females 70 patients owing to epilepsy or to feebleness of mind or body are unable to be allowed out of the wards or airing court, even to attend chapel: that is some 160 women walk beyond the grounds or are employed in the laundry and wash-house, or attend chapel. I believe the whole asylum is going on smoothly & without friction: which is greatly owing to our possessing a carefully selected & very respectable staff of servants all round, as well as the great liberty allowed to the Inmates – These being at this time only 122 out of 465 patients who are unable to leave the wards or airing courts; or, only about one quarter of the insane.'[46] 10th May 1882

'The walk around Home Farm land is nearly completed & looks very well; being covered with fine cinders, procured at the gas works at 8d a load, the path will always be dry & serviceable and together with a path around the Cricket Field will afford a "Promenade" of about ¾ of a mile for the patients. The women will take their walk in the morning & the men after dinner. This will enable the airing courts to be emptied daily almost entirely in compliance with the expressed wishes of the Commissioners for Lunacy.'[47] 11th October 1882

45 Leicestershire & Rutland Lunatic Asylum Medical Journal DE3533-277

46 Superintendent's Journal DE3533-86

47 Superintendent's Journal DE3533-86

The walks were then organised in single sexed groups and at specific times of the day, so that female or male parties would not meet each other, & were potentially very therapeutic activities. Ann (189/2117) was one patient where active employment and frequent out door exercise sufficed to free her from most of her melancholia and she left the asylum in good health. Many were even allowed to walk into town for a variety of purposes. They went out on their word that they would return. Arthur (187/1513) a solicitor having given his 'parole d'honneur' that he would not escape, was allowed to go beyond the bounds of the Asylum unattended. Certain patients were actually allowed a key so that they had free exit beyond the grounds. Elizabeth (197/4557) a 'cab proprietress' frequently went out from the hospital for drives with her son. Individuals like Samuel (196/4339) & Thomas (190/2339) were trusted to have days out with their friends. A Mary (191/2835) went out with a nurse to see her friends getting married. John (217CCBP3) a farm bailiff from Melton Mowbray though, had to be stopped from walking into town, as he became very troublesome, going into banks and other places. In February 1864, an elderly patient was assaulted on a road near the asylum and robbed of twenty-five shillings, the response of the asylum management was not to tighten supervision and restrict patients' movement, but it decided instead to improve the street lighting along the road (3533/84).

There were picnics at various locations ranging from the Asylum's own cricket field or lawns to Bradgate Park. One absolutely incredible, totally amazing, picnic was recorded at the Newton Unthank Asylum farm 13th June 1883. The 1881 Census, confirms just how close the Asylum Farm was for rail access, as next door to the farm, lived the Gateman for the Midland Railway & his neighbour was the Railway Pointsman: -

> '... we reached a kind of climax yesterday when, with the knowledge of Mr Woodcock we held a monster picnic & some 350 of the Patients & staff were taken to the Farm at Newtown Unthank by a Special train from the Welford Road Siding – The train left at 1.p.m. and returned from Desford at 7.p.m. The party were supplied with tea, cake, bread & butter & cold meat at about ½ past three in the afternoon. The Patients were seated in two separate Camps; the sexes apart. A Large tent, which had been leant to us kindly by Mr Billson, Belgrave Rd was erected in case of rain; and we took our attendants band of music – The day was everything that could be desired; the Party behaved very well, and all apparently enjoyed themselves immensely – Not a single mishap or unpleasantness occurred – Mr H C Woodcock honoured us for an hour in the afternoon. We all reached home safely at 7.30 pm very thankful at having completed our anxious undertaking & at having carried through to a successful issue what I think may be considered as quite an unprecedented excursion. The success of the undertaking was due in great measure to the fact that our Station at Welford Road siding was so close to the Asylum (being only 200 yards distant) & is so private. Secondly to the possession of our own Estate at Newtown to picnic upon – Finally, the patients were extremely manageable, perhaps because during the last 6 months, they have been allowed so much liberty & have been so little locked up.' Reported in journal entry dated 13th June 1883.[48]

It must have been a picnic worth recording as the date of the journal entry is exactly the same date as the actual picnic. This grand picnic happened again in July 1884. Other entertaining activities were also organised both inside & outside the gates. Daniel (196/4229) a Roman Catholic Priest eventually

---

48 Superintendent's Journal DE3533-86

became well enough to go to theatres and concerts with one of the asylum doctors. A patient named Henry (190/2438) from Ashby who had at one time been a monk living at St Bernard's Monastery & he was given leave to visit the Holy Cross Chapel, but he always returned punctually at the appointed time. One of the most important parts of the asylum timetable was the live entertainment that was arranged, to enjoy both inside & outside the asylum. Thanks to the kindness of the lessees over a hundred patients would go to watch the annual pantomimes, which took place at the Theatre Royal or the Opera House. After one performance at the Opera House, each of the male patients was presented with one ounce of tobacco, a pipe and an orange. There were also theatrical performances within the Asylum itself, usually in the recreation room, which included the various amateur dramatic groups, the Leicester Black & White Pierrots in December 1909, and 64 children from Clarendon Park School also performed for the patients. There were the Punch & Judy shows, or artists performing conjuring tricks, comical acts, ventriloquism or exhibitions of pictures and a celebrated harpist Mr Aptommas came to perform. There were also lectures on Heavenly Bodies & on various wonders in Earth & Sea, illustrated by limelight & a magic lantern. Tickets or free passes were also given for patients to visit Leicestershire Agricultural Show held on the Race Course or an Exhibition at the Floral Hall. On 19th June 1869 'the proprietors of Henry & Adams Circus invited the patients to witness their exhibition and 75 of the more orderly patients were enabled to avail themselves of this invitation'.[49]

The front lawns were also used for strategic sports activities.

Photograph of Asylum Staff's Dramatic Performance. Stewart Collection courtesy of ROLLR.

49 Superintendent's Journal DE3533-84

'1st Jan 1855 In the summer time several weekly assemblages of the industrious patients and those who were capable of enjoyment took place on the lawn in front of the asylum when the Amusements of Dancing, Bowls, Quoits & other popular sports afforded them great satisfaction – On these occasions it has been the custom with certain limitations to associate both sexes in my judgement with the best possible results.' [50]

On 1st August 1871 a number of patients were allowed under careful supervision to witness the Athletic Sports, which were held on the field adjoining the Asylum. Every opportunity was taken when appropriate for patients to join in sports outdoors. Football games & cricket matches are both mentioned within the case notes. Charles (203/6135) a hosiery hand worked on the farm in the day & enjoyed a game of cricket in the evening. In 1893 there was a cricket match between the doctors & parsons. Cricket was played and practised on most fine afternoons & evenings. John (217CCBP33) a grocer from London was recorded as unoccupied except for picking up tennis balls in the summer, but there is no record as to who was actually playing the game. The matches also afforded patients the opportunities to sit & watch. One of the best viewing stations must have been the scaffold specially erected for patients to look at the races in September 1856. Ann (188/1754) from Woodhouse had the misfortune though of injuring herself when she fell from it.

Upholding their religious beliefs was for most patients an absolutely essential component of their lives within the asylum. A high proportion of patients chose to go to services held in the Asylum's own Chapel. Up until November 1864 the Chapel had been without any means of being heated but the Superintendent at that time put in a request for a gill stove.[51] The more musical activities within the chapel proved to be very therapeutic to the patients in general. In April 1862, it was decided to commence singing and chanting a portion of the service, the results being twofold. Firstly, the behaviour of the congregation became remarkably good and secondly a very large proportion of the patients ended up grinning during the responses. [52] The Chapel patients could also follow their religious beliefs through the Asylum library facilities. Benjamin (187/1486) a printer occupied himself by reading the Testament or the Bible & sought the greatest quiet within his reach. As books were unfortunately often the first target of destruction the superintendent frequently had to request permission for new books: -

'I shall be glad of your permission to obtain some books for the patients library as I find that 106 of the books have been lost or destroyed. I anticipate that the expense of procuring suitable books for this purpose will not exceed £10.00.'[53] 12th March 1862

The Bible though was inevitably the most important publication, regardless of the specific religions of the time within Leicestershire. A framework knitter from Enderby was recorded as: -

'To have been paying measurably great attention to his religious duties at his Baptist Chapel of which he is a member - The sight of a common print of our saviour excites very violent conduct.' (187/1476)

---

50 Superintendent's Journal DE3533-83

51 Superintendent's Journal DE3533-84

52 Superintendent's Journal DE3533-84

53 Superintendent's Journal DE3533-84

The Holy Book for many, regardless of whether they were a mental patient or not, was a tremendous potential source of comfort. Eliza (197/4457) from Melton Mowbray was constantly reading a religious book in the hope that she might find that same comfort. Several patients would spend the whole day reading testaments or the bible. John (192/3019) from Bradford, Yorkshire was very fond of opening five Bibles at once and Ann (187/1416) from Newton Burgoland frequently read the Bible aloud. George (202/5870) from Deacon's Lane, Ibstock, when in the airing court would treat his hearers to a sermon on behalf of the Salvation Army in which he had once held a commission.

There were also the recuperative activities inside the walls. Some patients chose uplifting activities with just a pen or pencil. Elizabeth (186/1074) for example a charwoman from Leicester would write poetry by the yards. William (206/65) a labourer from Loughborough would present samples of his poetry to the staff. Christopher (193/3300) a druggist from Great Glen, was fond of drawing small objects, which he had seen in illustrated papers. Mary (200/5317) from Oakham had completed some magnificent pencil drawings from prints, which she gave to the medical officers. James Murray (198/4822) the architectural surveyor's magnificent sketch of the Asylum survives to this day.[54] Thomas (186/1092) a grocer from Castle Donington was a great bookworm and was much engrossed with Dr Chalmer's, Bridgewater Treatise and made copious notes in the margins. Another James (188/1669) occupied himself with the paper rather than the mark makers and would make the most peculiar paper & stick pipes daily. William (195/3963) a framework knitter from Loughborough busied himself making a model of a cogwheel. Some patients enjoyed playing cards, dominoes, billiards or bagatelle.

The Library (date of photograph unknown). Stewart Collection courtesy of ROLLR.

---

54 James Murray Sketch of the Asylum See Introductory Image.

For most music was wonderful therapy. Several patients like Sarah (193/3381) from Kimcote joined the chapel choir on Sundays. William (195/4050) an imbecile was not as fortunate as Sarah in being allowed to join the choir, as he is recorded as having- 'a voice like a nutmeg grater.' After a few brass instruments were purchased a brass band was put together, composed of both attendants and patients. The group were then able after 'arriving at some excellence' to furnish the patients with dance music which gave them 'unfailing amusement'. One of the most strategic arrivals at the asylum was a French Piano in or around 1846. The instrument enabled the resident medical officer, to establish dancing twice a week, which he believed, 'assisted him considerably in his curative measures'. Some of the patients would quite enjoy themselves just dancing alone at dances or the weekly ball when there was one. (In February 1865 there is reference to a weekly ball in one of the patients case notes (191/2578)). There were two very special celebratory occasions. One was the customary Christmas Ball for the patients & their friends in the Entertainment Room. There was plumb cake & port wine with several songs being sung at the conclusion of the dancing. There were the usual annual presents of handkerchiefs, scarves being given to about 80 female patients, who are employed usefully and about the same number of workers among the men received presents of tobacco, pipes, snuff boxes & scarves. The other festive activity was the servants' ball that took place at the end of the year & it was reported that all the staff behaved well & 'expressed themselves as being greatly pleased with the treat'. The supper was at 11 pm & the dancing concluded at 2 am.

Photograph of the Recreation Room Christmas 1890's. Stewart Collection courtesy of ROLLR.

Not everyone was able to safely join in absolutely every asylum leisure activity. It was quite a formidable task to provide daily entertainments for those with more permanent congenital defects. The admission of idiots or imbeciles to the County Asylum did not always involve just completely negative feedback. A major part of any form of cure was any activity, that a patient could be usefully employed in, or appropriately entertained by, regardless of their individual mental ability or condition. For some a very basic plaything like a doll, a book, or a bunch of keys would provide basic entertainment, day in and out. Ida (211/71) an idiot who was both deaf & dumb, from Narborough, 'would play for hours with needle & cotton & thread beads'. Another Ida (199/5023) from Melton loved it when she was taken for a run by one of the staff. Mary Louisa (210/8) from Uppingham is recorded as spending the whole of her time 'polishing a piece of tin'. Mary (192/2855) from East Norton was lucky that, 'There is another little girl about her size who makes a good play fellow for her'. William (195/3852) from Ratcliffe Culey was fond of playing with a ball & asked for a peg top but could not spin it. Elizabeth (212/30) an imbecile from Enderby, has two photographs of herself within the asylum. In the second photograph she has been given a pair of spectacles to wear & looks exceedingly smart in them. Archibald (202/5841) loved going to the dances and would sit rocking to the rhythm of the music, he also enjoyed the chapel choral services, but morning prayers could not successfully entertain him. The really young handicapped male children were often located in the female sections as they were often quite successfully cared for & entertained by the female patients. James (194/3686) from Earl Shilton's health became so delicate that he was very purposefully placed in the Female Ward 1 for a short period. Cecil (204/23) a four year old from Market Harborough who could not walk & whose only word was 'Mamma', was also much petted & nursed by the female patients. Relationships with older female patients were not always effective. Annie (203/6115) an elderly imbecile from Ashby, showed an obsessive interest in a small idiot girl, whom she dragged about with her everywhere. Mary (218/303) from Syston took a great fancy to a young imbecile child, actually believing that she was its mother & followed the little girl everywhere too. Some of the highly mentally defective would not take any interest in others except some idiots equal to themselves. At times the future prospects of the congenitally defective would be quite negatively reviewed: -

> 'This is a case of congenital imbecility of great degree - so much so that it is scarcely to be expected that his very confirmed bad habits will be eradicated or that he can be made a useful member of society ... his malady is attributed to an injury he received falling down stairs many years ago.' (187/1610)

An individual's occupation was one of the most important roles within their lives & even some of the idiot and imbecile patients had an occupation of some sort before their entry. Harriett's (190/2496) diminutive appearance had though sadly led to her being exhibited about the country as a 'Talking Monkey'. Most incoming, retarded, male patients had been ordinary labourers and given tasks that were suited to their abilities, such as tending cattle, but some became too excited or passionate whilst performing these basic duties. Frank (198/4899) had apparently been taught both carpentry and boot making previously at the Earlswood Asylum. Several of those with minimal mental capacities from birth were able to make themselves useful within the daily routines of the Asylum, many being very useful within the wards themselves. To take just one example Sarah (193/3252) from Barrow waited most patiently on an old epileptic lady. Some were very industrious assisting in the general very necessary cleaning of the wards. Sarah (201/5413) from Woodhouse could be persuaded to darn stockings or do a little other sewing at times. Sarah Ann (195/3928) an imbecile employed her time in crocheting garters. Ruth (189/1998) from Melton made herself very useful within the washhouse or laundry. Others made themselves useful in the kitchen, scullery, making beds and later on in the new bake house. James (192/2843) an idiot from Thurlaston, was very willing to do anything that he was able to do and one of his main tasks was to lead the more helpless patients to the table at meal times.

A significant proportion of the mentally handicapped asylum inmates were found occupations outdoors. Wherever possible total respect was afforded to each of their interests and capabilities. William (190/2407) from Barrow was very fond of animals so he was assigned to work in the piggeries, being rewarded with pieces of tobacco. They were not any old brand of pig that William helped care for; there were the 'Berkshire Porkels' or the 'White Yorkshires'. (It was not just the humans who were struck down with illness, for in April 1885 Swine Fever broke out in the piggeries after some pigs had eaten some nightshade which had got in with the potato stalks which they ate). On 20th May 1878 John (194/3614) from Aylestone was actually placed within a kind of apprenticeship with the gardener.

Quite a degree of trust was afforded to the imbeciles who went to work out on the distant farm. Charles (193/3217) an imbecile from Uppingham had been a farm labourer and a criminal before admission. On arrival he was soon given a position on the asylum farm, where he was always very well behaved lad and worked both steadily and regularly. He worked exceptionally well at chopping wood. Not all attempts to train idiot or imbecile inmates to an occupation were successful. If they could be very violent toward their attendants within the asylum grounds, then it is understandable that the farm servants usually seemed unwilling to take them out to the farm. In December 1896 it was questioned in the Superintendent's Journal whether the attendants accompanying any type of patient to the asylum farm should be' watching or working'. An asylum outdoors worker generally escorted those patients working at the farm, both to and from there.

Several imbecile patients though were given the task of a messenger to outside the asylum walls with no escort whatsoever. One of the patients so frequently climbed over the hospital walls, that he was eventually given a more positive role to his clambering, by being given the job of a messenger over the fortifications. It is not clear which side of the wall he was carrying the messages to (194/3578)? One patient had to have his messenger job curtailed when it was discovered that he had stolen stamps out of the office & another messenger was more fortunate in retaining his occupation even though he would frequently have had too much 'to drink' when sent on errands.

Thomas (193/3210) had been born with a congenital defect, which was of sufficient severity to prevent him following an occupation, and he had for 8 to 9 years been an inmate to Lutterworth Union. His history of working tasks within the asylum highlights the variety of tasks that would be assigned to the idiot & imbecile patients to help to develop their life skills and confidence: -

'1/7/1872 he is employed in the wards in domestic matters - July 8th employed on the farm 27/8/1877 No epilepsy reported for 12 months past - Works at Garden House 7/6/1883 occupied in the kitchen and elsewhere can be trusted anywhere - mentally unchanged 8/1/1894 Goes down town on messages ...useful imbecile goes errands well.' 10/7/1900

It appears to have been far more of an achievement to have got the less mentally skilled to learn an indoor trade. Needham (187/1348) was taught weaving and shoemaking but neither of the patterns of training was of any use. One patient George (195/3929) from Loughborough vehemently refused to become either a tailor or a shoemaker. Nathaniel (193/3259) an imbecile was though recorded as working well within the 'new workshops' in July 1872. Michael (194/3578) from Gilmorton had been given the occupation of a painter, whilst in the asylum but he was eventually unable to leave the Asylum in consequence of him not having sufficient intelligence to gain his own livelihood. It was considered that if he could be put with any man to direct & live with him - he would do well outside, but he stayed within the 'asylum' the place of 'safety'.

Others, who were not mentally handicapped, had problems with physical disabilities, which made performing many asylum daily jobs too complex. Some were unable to give their tasks enough attention. John (198/4805) an elderly shoemaker used to do some work within the shoemaker's shop, but would frequently undo what he had achieved a few minutes afterwards. Many inmates were too restless to work successfully like Jane (197/4569) from Knossington who 'could not hold her attention to any task she was given'. Sarah (197/4523) from Belgrave's work was usually imperfect because she hurried too much on the tasks and they usually had to be done again. There were some inmates who wanted to work on certain tasks, but they were not well enough to do so. Sometimes patients could be badly behaved, have relapses or epileptic attacks whilst they were working. John (194/3553) a maltser had such severe chilblains, that he was unable to work at the farm during the coldest winter months. Margaret (192/2919) had to be brought back from the laundry due to her misconduct and Ann (190/2372) from Barrow caused similar problems by continually plastering her hair with soap whilst there. John (203/6202) who was previously a coach maker started to act strangely whilst in the carpenter's shop, so his work mates advised him to go back to the wards. Albert (200/5293) an epileptic would work on the farm when his health allowed him to do so. Catherine (196/4386) from Knighton had a similar problem with epilepsy but she would always endeavour to work when the fits were absent.

Not every patient was able to work in the more labour intensive asylum employment areas. Several women who attempted to work in the laundry or kitchen found it to be a little too much for them. For the frailer or elderly patients there were some lighter tasks such as dusting, scouring, watering flowers, darning stockings, working with straw, sewing or crocheting. Mary Ann (203/6187) originally admitted from Market Harborough Workhouse on 27th September 1900 to the Asylum with dementia was a very significant asylum patient. She was blind & had been ill for 5 years previous to her admission and she was a patient in the asylum for 7 years. During her curative stay she continued & withheld her occupation of making crocheted articles. She is featured 18 years later in a front-page newspaper article within the Illustrated Leicester Chronicle (Saturday 3rd October 1925), at the age of 74, with the Matron of the Market Harborough Poor Law Institution. The most strategic parts about this event are firstly that Mary Ann was still alive & apparently very contented & secondly that a member of staff saw the newspaper, took a cutting of it, and placed it where it still lies to this day within the case notes.[55] There were other easy tasks that could be given during the course of the day, such as carrying various articles, bed making, helping washing dishes, folding in the laundry, working in the linen room or pantry, putting the young ones to bed or helping with feebler patients. George (188/1786) was very

55 The photograph is unfortunately in too poor a condition to include in this publication

113

'methodical and trustworthy employed in taking luncheons to the male side'. Charles (185/647) would make himself useful with various tasks which included 'carrying coals'. Where possible patients were given tasks that their age and health would permit. Samuel (195/3825) from Willoughby was a good simple general hand within the kitchen. Many worked in the galleries and Rebecca (185/623) from Daventry, had an excellent reputation for cheerfully rendering assistance, in any way that she could. As patients got both better and stronger they were given occupations that involved more energy and skills. Benjamin from Croxton Kerrial was one such patient: -

'He was anxious for employment and various sundry little jobs were given him to do in the galleries at first, and finding he did not relapse, but kept steadily improving at his own urgent entreaty, employment was given him out of doors and for many weeks before he left the Institution (which he did quite recovered) he was a most industrious, and valuable workman in the garden.' (185/628)

The mentally handicapped & the more bodily frail patients were then given every feasible opportunity to have a go with certain asylum tasks. John (185/627) from Barlestone was not able to do labouring work but he was very useful in the Galleries and was extremely willing to do any thing in his power for the good of the Institution. It was obviously also imperative to find a work place within the asylum for the patients with more normal levels of intelligence & physical capabilities. John (196/4182) from Lutterworth who had been admitted as intemperate, was put to work the very next day after his admission. Initially, under the premise that patients when appropriate must be found a place for them to work, it was not immediately possible: -

'10/1/1854 It is much regretted that the want of workrooms in the Asylum does not permit that general employment by the patients in such occupations as shoemaking, tailoring … and stocking weaving – occupations which while they are normal in other County Asylums are to be regarded as a great means to curative treatment.' [56]

The situation did though improve: -

'1/1/1855 During the past year the employment of the Patients has considerably increased, the boots & shoes worn by them are made & repaired in the Asylum as is also the Clothing of the Male & Female patients with few exceptions.'[57]

Once more workshops were constructed or included, selected employment as an integral part of treatment within the asylum, became easier to allocate. Other younger inmates were often given occupational tasks in a form of an apprenticeship. The Superintendent & his staff though were still obliged to consider, even when patients were expressing a definite inclination towards work, the safety aspects involved in employing them. One of the surest ways for a patient to affect a swift discharge from the asylum was to be seen performing a job well for several weeks. Patients also often made specific requests such as Margaret from Market Harborough: -

---

56 Superintendent's Journal DE3533-83

57 Superintendent's Journal DE3533-83

'Requested today to work in the laundry. When I told her she had better ask the matron if there was room for her she lost her temper and became sulky.' (201/5576)

Many patients became assistants to the nurses or attendants and helped to care for certain other patients when it was considered to be appropriate. Edward (198/4897) a twenty-year-old imbecile from Harby, was one who would 'help to look after the boys'. The case books often record the young idiots and imbeciles being taken care of, by some elderly patients who adopted a type of parental role with them.

'This old man is constantly tending the idiot boys in Ward 1. It is quite a labour of love 28/8/1877.' John from Gilmorton (193/3299)

Photograph of haymakers probably close to the asylum itself & not at the Newtown Unthank Farm. Stewart Collection courtesy of ROLLR.

It was not just the men who looked after the mentally handicapped inmates. Eliza (194/3403) a housewife from Coalville, who was initially admitted with chronic mania, eventually whilst in recovery was able to look very kindly, after a young idiot. There were two principal sites for the men to work. One was work in the great outdoors & the other was in the asylum workshops. The availability of land to cultivate was of prime importance, when related to work for the men.

In 1877 the Asylum Committee were exceedingly concerned that the sale of 37 acres of land, together with a 30 foot wide strip being taken from the Occupation Road now University Road, would have a direct impact on employment opportunities for the male patients and that they would just end up pacing the airing courts. In 1870 more workshops & a new bakery were constructed, to help to modernise, increase & widen the employment opportunities. Going out to work on the Newtown Unthank Asylum Farm (which was about 7 miles distant from the asylum) was for the men, one of the best routes to an eventual cure. Patients who were accustomed to working on the asylum farm, were also given other outside jobs when called for, such as gravelling or asphalting walks around the fields in order to give patients more walking opportunities. The harvest supper in early autumn was taken as a reward for the heavy labour during the previous twelve months with often 70 to 80 patients taking part in this seasonal feast.

Photograph of the Assembly Hall. Stewart Collection courtesy of ROLLR.

The laundry was also an incredible hive of hot, hard work, for the asylum staff and patients who were required to be busy as bees. Several worked in the 'linen room' too.[58]

---

58   Patient Case Books DE3533-197/4434

'The increasing quantity of linen used in the asylum (now amounting to 4015 pieces per week) is more than the servants and patients can properly manage.' 10/12/1862[59]

The laundress and the patients in her charge, eventually were seen to require their own sleeping accommodation. Mary (197/4648) a seamstress from Oakham was in 1886 recorded as being warded at the laundry. Not all the patients could cope with the heat that was emitted from the procedures within the laundry. Ann (185/656) the ribbon weaver from Burton Hastings was in a bad state on admission being described as 'most wretched and despairing of ever finding a green spot in memory's waste.' She expressed a strong desire to work in the laundry where she made herself exceptionally useful. She suffered a slight relapse initially, with the temperatures within the laundry environment, but eventually got better. Emma (201/5585) was quoted as being brilliant at doing the ironing and Christiana was one of the most dedicated workers in the laundry: -

'This poor old creature might be called 'skin & grief' she works daily at the laundry like an automaton.' (187/1725-188/91)

Men would also be directed to help with the mangling of the wet washing. Elizabeth (198/4838) who worked in the laundry often had to be brought back when she became too excited, which was a far easier task than sending back problematic patients, from the farm, before the days work was done. The laundry workers also had their own special treat together with a few kitchen servants, by being taken in the summer for a picnic usually on a Thursday, to Bradgate Park.

The farm was not the only occupation for the great outdoors, there were other jobs where patients of both sexes were essentially 'out and about'. Outdoor jobs mentioned were, gate porters, gardening, lime washing, working with the lifting pump, attending the poultry, mowing lawns or working in the potato house. Henry (191/2690) from Quorndon was given the task of looking after the greenhouse boiler. Richard helped gathering apples and wheeling them to be stored. Ann (186/922) from Long Whatton became the actual keeper of the gate. Andrew (206/8) from Uppingham who credited himself in 'being the best vegetable grower in the world' had of course tremendous potential.

'Two male patients are now engaged in building a sunshade in No 2 Female Airing Court.' 12/1/1869 [60]

When and where the opportunities arose, then patients carried on their former occupations before admission such as continuing being a tailor, framework knitting at the stocking frames in the loom shop, bakery, carpentry, shoemaking, millinery, dressmaking, painting & decorating, glazing or assisting the stoker. In April 1871 one of the patients a baker by trade, made & baked some 10 stones of bread one day [61]. William (204/109) who had previously developed a business with a mobile photographic booth, made himself useful with his artistic skills, by making decorations for the ward at Christmas. William (187/1514) had potentially the most useful former occupation, as he was once an attendant at an Asylum. A basket maker (186/1176) from Kegworth made several baskets for the asylum before he left. John (187/1600) a wheelwright from Oldbury near Dudley made several

---

59 Superintendent's Journal DE3533-84

60 Superintendent's Journal DE3533-84

61 Superintendent's Journal DE3533-85

wheelbarrows before he left. Thomas (187/1643) a bricklayer proved himself useful in constructing new workrooms in 1855 and earned himself some wages with the builder for doing so. A pavier named William (189/2118) was at one time well employed in repairing the asylum back yard. Another William (185/616), a tailor from Northampton very industriously repaired a great deal of the patients' clothes. Eliza (194/3679) from Staunton Harold who had four children was brought in her own children's clothes to mend. Whereas, Joseph (192/2977) also a tailor was so inclined to tearing up his clothes that he was 'obliged to be kept away from the tailor's shop owing to his mischievous propensities'. The tailors obviously worked well for: -

> 'The stock of clothing made up in the store rooms appear to be sufficient for ordinary consumption of the asylum for at least 6 months. I have therefore employed the tailor in cleaning & restuffing the bed mattresses – and he with some 5 or 6 male patients is engaged upon this work in the new workshops.'[62] 12th June 1872

Some patients' improvement in health led to them taking up quite important roles and positions of relative responsibility within the asylum complex. Thomas (189/2078) from Hinckley was employed daily on the farm and most skilfully took charge of and managed the irrigation with liquid manure conducted by trenches cut with spade. George (202/5785) from Hugglescote actually became the headman in the bread room. It must not be overlooked that patients were in danger from occupational accidents within a trade both at home & whilst a patient within the asylum & John a former carpenter is mentioned within an Asylum Medical Journal as having on 21st March 1876 fallen from a ladder & bruised and cut his face.[63]

Several individuals were so used to being industrious that they just had to carry on working. Henry (193/3298) from Hemington who worked in the bakery and cleaned shoes was quoted as having 'a mania for work'. William (185/589) a carpenter from Loughborough could not be restrained even in unfavourable weather from working. Charles (199/5002) from Ullesthorpe was constantly asking to be set to a task. A labourer called Joseph (189/2083) had an even greater problem as he was driven by an incontrollable impulse to work, which he would do, from morning to night.

Some patients needed quite a degree of encouragement to get them to work. Jane (197/4650) from Great Easton took a considerable amount of persuading to work in the laundry. Attendants and nurses were sometimes put at risk when trying to encourage inmates with no leanings to getting up and working. Eliza (197/4548) from Broughton Astley made one such attack on one of the asylum nurses in April 1885. Sometimes the inmates were felt by the staff to be fit to work, but when they became violent to the attendants or site servants, then their occupational company, was at times exceptionally unwelcome. Often the tools required to perform a task placed both inmate and attendants in danger. Charles (195/4070) from Quorndon threatened an attendant with a potato-peeling knife in the vegetable house. Thomas (190/2375) from Wigston was the storekeeper's attendant for distributing beer and at times he was very clearly quite intoxicated and had to be sent back to the wards.

---

62 Superintendent's Journal DE3533-85

63 Medical Journal DE3533-277

Unfortunately, many had disinclination towards employment & could or would not be placed within any asylum-linked task. Several patients earned themselves quite negative comments for their attitude towards work: -

'Is quite unoccupied except in carrying out her antics' (198/4907)
'This young man is eradically idle - He never reads or employs himself in any way - he loafs his existence' (195/3783)
'Suffers from the lazybones disease' (195/3820)
'The greatest apathy and pusillanimity prevailing' (186/1110)
'She dresses herself and sits upon the same seat nearly all day long' (189/2164)

Charles from Long Whatton had a problem of religious dimensions: -

'Was put to work to feed the pigs and he said the following Monday that he felt so wretched at the dreadful crime he had committed of working on the Sabbath that he could not do anything more.' (191/2787)

Several patients refused to do a task due to their claim that they should not have been in the asylum anyway. There were those who believed that if they worked they should receive wages for doing so. Emma a housewife from Quorndon had a completely different approach: -

'Attempts to make money by putting a card in the window with the inscription mangling done here.' (201/5585)

Hannah (190/2485) from Broughton Astley specifically asked to work in the scullery but insisted that 'she should be paid for working there'. Sampson (196/4158) from Loughborough declared that he was only being kept in as a patient because he was just too useful.

A few became so contented, felt so safe and settled, within the asylum that they were often allowed, once officially cured, to stay on as workers if they requested to do so. Mary (185/613) from Newton Linford was one such patient who remained as a household servant. Charlotte from Belgrave followed a similar pattern: -

'This patient has lived several years in service but left all her places in a very unsatisfactory manner and eventually led a life of great irregularity her habits have been very intemperate - She was employed in the house as a domestic servant and her services were most useful at her period of quitting the Establishment approached she became very desponding and earnestly solicited employment which she was at length given her and she remained cheerfully working for the Institution merely for her board.' (185/745)

An individual's educational abilities appear to have had little if anything to do with the choice of occupation they were given. Even though an ability to read & write appeared to be viewed as quite a positive quality for patients to possess. In general terms, almost half the new admissions could read & write. For just under half of those on admission, their reading & writing skills were either not known or not recorded. A very small percentage of the arrivals are recorded as having no reading and writing ability at all. At times the range of an individuals ability to read & write was more precisely included. Three patients - John (195/4001) a brewer's agent from Spinney Hill Rd & two ladies named Mary (217CCBP117-217CCBP49)- one from Osgathorpe & the other a governess from Leicester were all recorded as being 'well educated'. Another two women called Mary - a retired excise officer's daughter (193/3376) from Stathern & a governess from Deal (217CCBP93) had their reading & writing skills recorded as being 'very good'. Several had their reading & writing skills more negatively defined as being 'defective', 'doubtful', 'dissipated' or 'deficient', 'scanty', 'indifferent' or 'imperfect'. John (198/4836) was an organist who could only read raised type. Walter (200/5300) a shoemaker from Oakham, William (199/5135) another shoemaker from Swinford near Rugby and James (199/5030) a miller from Sheepy Magna were all only capable of writing their name. George (197/4555) a higgler from Earl Shilton had his education skills recorded as 'almost nil'. Whereas Mary (192/2940) from Loughborough 'no education at all'. In the later case books it is evident that the patients (with the exception of those with congenital disorders) were generally expected to be able to read & write. Priscilla (197/4721) from Knighton was criticised in 1887 for preventing her children from going to school. Elizabeth (210/139) from Wigston was admitted in June 1903. By this time the majority patients would be expected to both read & write - Elizabeth told the doctor – 'that a European king had been killed by his wife who was a clairvoyant and that, ' he should find all the details in an ordinary daily newspaper which she gave me to read.'

One of the most important routes of recovery, was eventually to be getting back to the home that many longed for. It was imperative to maintain outside contact with that very world that they were hopefully going to return to one day. For patients such as young Emily (196/4265) the idiot <u>foundling</u> (as underlined in case book) or the wanderers, who were completely unknown to anyone but themselves, this was going to be a virtually impossible task. For many, liaisons with the other side of the walls involved pen ink & paper. James (198/4987) from Thurmaston North constantly wanted to send telegrams home to his family. Several patients were encouraged to write to their immediate relatives so as to maintain reasonable contact. Eliza (188/1749) from London wrote a very proper and coherent letter to her husband. Mary Jane (192/2877) from Braunston was persuaded to write to her husband for him to come & see her. As well as outgoing post there was the mail in too. Arrangements were made for Elizabeth (201/5479) a nurse maid from Beverley in Yorkshire to go home after a telegram arrived from her mother saying that she was coming to fetch her. John a Wesleyan minister from Castle Donington wrote long letters to,

> '... the Queen the Archbishop of Canterbury and the president of the Congregational Conference requesting to remove him hence and to provide him with a well endowed benefice in which his universal talents will be appreciated.' (201/5540)

Mary's (190/2389) husband a grocer was so anxious to have her home, that he signed an order for her discharge and took her home the same day. Sally (198/4804) from Gilmorton's husband was satisfied with her behaviour and he desired to have her home. Some relatives appeared to show some form of guilt complex in their family member having the need to go to an asylum and Susan (201/5563) from Earl Shilton was ultimately discharged at the urgent request of her husband, who said he was now able to look after her. Fanny (217CCBP157) the clergyman's wife from Kings Norton was similarly discharged by the authority of her husband, the Superintendent was strongly against this decision as he himself felt that Fanny was not yet ready to go home. Thomas's (199/5033) wife from Melton Mowbray strongly requested that he be allowed home, so that she was able to nurse him & he actually died the next day at home of senile decay. For a few it was errors or problems with the official paper work, which would give early access to their home environments. Both Joseph (199/5049) from Ratby & Harriett (199/5050) from Loughborough were discharged in consequence of lapses in their certificates. Elizabeth (193/3296) from Long Clawson was released due to informalities with her certificate. These are just three examples of problems with paper work.

For many contact was maintained by their family & their own friends coming to visit them. The visits from relatives were usually made once a fortnight. Some parts of Leicestershire were over thirty miles from the asylum; this distance could have posed real practical problems for those wishing to visit persons confined. Maria (194/3422) from Smeeton Westerby was much satisfied & relieved by a visit from her husband & children. When Mary's (195/4002) husband came to visit her from Whitwick, he 'was very pleased to find her clothed and in her right mind'. John (193/3225) was visited by a visitor whom he had not seen for years and he was much pleased with her visit. The visits did not always go well and Elizabeth (190/2310) from Woodhouse was much worse & maniacal after any interviews with her husband on his visits. Maria (195/3964) from Hinckley's husband had visited one Saturday, but following his visit, she did not express any immediate desire to return home. Frederick (200/5332) a bricklayer from Kibworth Beauchamp had completely the opposite tactics when his family visited, 'Very anxious to go home, on visits from his relatives, tried to frighten them into getting him out, threatening to commit suicide.' A lady named Cassandra's memory had been almost obliterated: -

> 'She does not even remember her fathers name ...makes no sign of recognition when he visits her.' (188/1777)

It did not help both patients & staff, when visitors did not arrive to schedule, especially if they were the official visitors or guardians, who were arriving to do one of their continual check ups: -

> 'Oct 14th 1908 a deputation from the Shardlow Board of Guardians visited this Asylum on Sept 17th. Their patients were collected for them at 2pm – the time of their appointment, but the deputation did not arrive until nearly 4.00 pm In the meantime the patients were sent back to the wards - it being considered that they were not coming. Hence there was some delay and a good deal of trouble in collecting the patients again, upon the arrival of the deputation.'[64]

There were many who had enough health within their body system, to long to be back home again with their families. If they had the muscular energy as well, then the most desperate usually absconded, rather than wait to be officially released. Harriet (201/5548) from Beresford Street in Coalville and Mary Jane (217CCBP135) from Belgrave were just two amongst many longing or begging to go home, but were not at the time of asking well enough to do so. A framesmith named Albert (202/5797) looked 'forward to going home to pick his gooseberries.' Elizabeth (191/2822) a nurse from Leicester was insistent on being discharged, but was eventually very relieved that her request was not complied with. A gentleman's usher from Gumley (196/4340) looked forward to getting home soon and declared 'that six weeks in the asylum would drive him off his head.' There was always for many the stigma of being a patient at an asylum & Ann Amelia from Loughborough, who had become quieter, was looking forward to being admitted to a convalescent home. (201/5551)

---

64 Superintendent's Journal DE3533-90

There were many patients who went out on day trips to be with the relatives. Mary (187/1500) a schoolmistress from Eaton Street in Leicester frequently went home on Sundays. A framework knitter from Earl Shilton was allowed to go down to town with his friends. (195/3896) The hope of going home again one day, could be a tremendous pick me up for a patient, & was reinforced through the knowledge that others had done so. For some the trip was for more tragic circumstances. Jane (198/4942) from Humberstone went out one day in the charge of a nurse to see her husband who was said to be dying. Alice (200/5402) from Markfield was summoned home on the sudden & unexpected death of her father.

Usually, the day trips home for convalescent inmates were both part of the reconnecting process & testing, or assessing abilities to cope again, outside the asylum. John (190/2437) a tailor from Great Wigston was allowed home to visit his children and returned at the appointed hour. Zilpah (197/4537) from Oadby who was taken dangerously ill 3 days after her confinement, would go home frequently to see her father for the day. George (193/3372) a horse clipper & hairdresser from Lutterworth, would regularly spend alternate Sundays with relations. Some times extended families enabled the trials out to take place and William (190/2361) from Thornton would go out on weekly visits to his uncle. Samuel (196/4339) from Walcote also had a day out with friends. William (193/3197) from Loughborough went home twice to see his friends and his visits that were financed by the friends,were very advantageous to him. The day trips out did not always go to plan & Charles (195/4012) a draughtsman from Aylestone was allowed to spend a day at home. When it got dark the same Charles hid himself & remained hidden until 11 pm when he returned, having to be brought back by his father & the police. Elizabeth (218CCBP351) from Great Bowden was taken out to a wedding, but was exceptionally upset on her return to the asylum.

For some patients both their own improving health & family circumstances allowed them to be away from the asylum for more than a day. Young Frederick (200/5340) admitted with simple mania from Wigston Magna was allowed home for a week at Christmas. Alfred (203/6164) from Oadby was also at home for a few days at Christmas time and he was quiet and well conducted. There was John (200/5366) though from Thurmaston on the other hand, who refused to go home to his relatives for the same seasonal celebration. Levy (200/5287) from Enderby left the asylum on a month's trial with both his wife and mother. At times 'a change of air – a holiday' was recorded within the records for Charity Patients. Charles (217CCBP11) a gentleman from Crediton appeared to have received much benefit from going to spend a week in Leamington with his attendant (assumedly private). John (217CCB/35) from Atherstone went to Dawlish for a fortnight also with his attendant. Before her admission Martha had tried 'a change of air in Stratford' for four months to no avail. (199/5032)

Many whilst out on leave, went looking for jobs, to take up on their eventual full release. John (189/2193) a stoker from Leicester, had great pleasure in bringing back the news that he could 'have employment at his old factory again'. William (201/5464) from Hinckley managed to procure himself some work in a foundry in Leicester & was therefore discharged. Thomas (194/3588) was promised a job at the gas works. An imbecile from Hinckley named Ann was recorded, 'She is desirous of getting a place of service and was therefore discharged this day to enable her to do so.' (190/2395) Most trials in the outside world went well. Annie (197/4549) though attempted to drown herself and had to be brought back. Things did not go well for Ellen from Loughborough who went out for a months trial in August 1894: -

'This morning a little before ten, she walked into the asylum and rang the laundry bell and asked to be readmitted. She explained her conduct by saying that she could not face the world outside or live in the poor home her husband provided for her: that she had strong impulses to do away with herself but as she didn't wish to die she preferred to come back to the asylum, consequently when her husband was out at work, she slipped out of the house quietly and took the train for Leicester. We found her a good deal agitated and shedding tears'. (201/5508)

Even for those who reached the 'free' outside world again the cure had perhaps not happened, for Mary (185/625) from Loughborough had not been home a fortnight, when she resumed all her former intemperate habits. Thomas (206/65) from the Greyhound Inn at Botcheston had only been home three weeks when he took his own life. Sophia (185/694) a blacksmith's wife appears to have relapsed soon after her discharge, she became restless & uneasy wandering from home without any settled purpose and even began to take a dislike to her children. Lucy (211/3) from Kibworth Beauchamp: -

'A week or so after her last discharge from here - she appeared at the lodge gates thirsty & foot sore - having apparently walked from home & asked to be taken in as she was unhappy at home - she was taken in by the police & the Leicester Workhouse & then transferred to her own Union, where she stayed two months & made herself very useful - always working. She was taken out by her husband 10 days ago - but returned 3 days later - quite changed mentally - dull, silent, refusing her food - has remained much the same since.'

There were other negative aspects in the return to former lives. One of the biggest problems was the official friends & not the asylum staff, deciding it was time for a patient to be discharged: -

'... in the mean time steps will be adopted to prevent for the future the friends from injudiciously interfering in the removal of Patients before the time when they may leave the asylum without fear of relapse.' (185/696)

Young Sarah (185/737) from Mountsorrel was discharged at the request of her friends – 'she was much improved but scarcely convalescent'. For several patients it was not clear if they had had any trial leave sessions or they were just deemed well enough to be in the outside world once more. Alice's (200/5232) mother from Kirby Muxloe had her discharged by special request, for she felt she could look after her. Mary from Ashby fortunately had a sister who had undertaken to take charge of her. Charlotte (199/5015) had conducted herself rationally since her last report, so she was taken by one of the nurses to her mother in Birmingham. Another Charlotte from Bishops Stortford, was removed from the institution and placed in lodgings in Leicester under the care of 'a proper person to attend to her.' (185/742)

Michael (197/4450) a compositor was fit to be discharged, but he had no clothes of his own to be sent out with. Henry (196/4228) from Foxton went home for a few days but returned of his own account as he had 'found that he was not particularly welcome there'. When John's (194/3455) father came to collect him from Walcote, he refused to go with him. Mary Jane (201/5425) from Kirby Bellars had to be discharged to the Workhouse as her relatives declined to have anything to do with her.

For many like Mary Jane, it was not home but the Workhouse - Thomas (185/754) & Elizabeth (185/733) both headed in that direction as they became classed as 'harmless incurable lunatics'. Several larger workhouses like Hinckley had their specific 'lunatic wards'.

Sadly, for many that contact with the outside world was not going to be the journey back home to their friends & relatives. As aforementioned hundreds of individuals maintained their status of patients & were relocated to other asylums or union workhouses. At least 40 patients are recorded as being sent out to Leicestershire County Union workhouses of Blaby, Barrow, Hinckley, Lutterworth, Market Harborough or Melton Mowbray. Esther (210/67) from Earl Shilton had been discharged to a workhouse and her husband had not been to see her there. Three patients William (185/755) from Burbage, Thomas (185/754) from Hinckley (in 1846) & Ann (185/790) from Sapcote (in 1851) were all discharged quite specifically to Hinckley Union Lunatic ward in the middle years of the 19th Century. Some were transferred to distant workhouses. A man named John (201/5416) a riveter, was relocated to Paddington workhouse.

The nearest asylum to be relocated to was the Borough Asylum in Humberstone, which opened 2nd September 1869. Ten patients, including Clarissa a glove stitcher, were actually transferred there on its opening day. (191/2824) Almost two hundred patients were transferred to the only asylum that was relatively close in distance. For the older patients though, who were transferred to the Borough Asylum from the County Asylum, after it's opening, really felt that they were being removed from their home.[65]

Patients were not just being transferred to workhouses or asylums within Leicestershire. There appear to be various bargaining processes in the establishment of contracts & arrangements with other mental institutions, due principally to building alterations or a lack of space. The other asylums mentioned in the case books are Bedford, Abingdon Abbey & Berry Wood (both in Northampton), Beverley, Bracebridge (Lincoln), Buckinghamshire, Burnley, Camberwell Greater London, Chatham (Kent), Claybury (London), Clifton Asylum (York), Colney Hatch (London), Denbigh (North Wales), Littlemore & Mickleover (both Derby), Devon, Dorset, Grove Hall (East London), Hatton (Warwickshire), Hereford, Huddersfield, Kent, Knowle (Hampshire), Lancaster, Macclesfield, Menston (Yorkshire), Middlesex, Nottingham, Somerset & Bath (at Wells), Stafford, Stothes Hall, Suffolk, Surrey, Sussex, Wadsley Sheffield, Wakefield, Whittington & Worcester. There were several relocations with Berrywood Northampton. The Leicestershire asylum must have been bursting at the seams in the summer of 1897 for the biggest recorded exodus to other asylums was the relocation of fifteen patients to Beverley Asylum in On 21st July 1897 and eleven patients to Wadsley Asylum Sheffield & on 5th August 1897. In July 1890 Kate (197/4597) who normally dwelt in Knighton, was moved to the Borough Asylum as a place had become available there.

Within the asylum contracts, patients with every form of mental condition were replaced, such as idiocy, imbecility, melancholia, mania or the more specific simple mania & chronic mania. One wonders if opportunities were taken to relocate the long term, more incurable patients in other asylums? Maria (192/2890) a framework knitter from Hinckley, who was relocated to Beverley, had been a patient suffering from melancholia for 29 years. John (194/3518) a bricklayer from Atherstone had been a patient with chronic mania for 31 years and was also relocated to Beverley. Movement from A to B was usually by horse and various forms of carriage, but transportation by rail also played

---

65   Leicestershire & Rutland Lunatic Asylum 1869 Annual Report

a part in the later relocation processes. Mental illness was everywhere and the right authority, usually the place of an individual's settlement, was expected to finance that treatment. There was of course eventually the movement of patients to the newly built asylum at Narborough in 1907 (Which was given the name of Carlton Hayes circa 1939). The County Asylum lay empty & untended after the inmates left in1908 – the paupers left in February & March, the charity clients left in August & September.

There are some incidents recorded where individuals were given financial assistance to allow them to have a more practical opportunity to return to life outside the asylum when they had recovered. To mention just a few found, there was George (185/726) a plasterer from Leicester was allowed 5/- a week when he was ultimately discharged on a month's trial. The guardians had allowed John (193/3277) from Oakham, 6 shillings and 9 pence a week. Francois (189/2051) a teacher was given £2.00 when he left from the Adelaide Fund & Joseph (190/2531) a bricklayer received £1 from the same fund.

The length of time a patient had to stay within the asylum is also obviously of great significance. Any statistics now given for the length of stay of patients, with relation to cure exclude all those who were aged 61 or over at the time of admission & any patient who was initially admitted as an idiot or imbecile. Almost a hundred patients had exceptionally short case book records, ranging from a few hours to thirty days. It is not always clear for the cause of this brief spell within care, but for a few the reasons are clearly given within the case books. For many it was just a change of class to 'Charity' or 'Independent', the consequence being a change of book. Joseph (187/1527) from Loughborough though was so critically ill, that his friends were advised that he would be best back home with his family. For a widowed lady from Leicester, no suitable treatment could be envisaged & she was therefore relocated within a workhouse (188/1828). Anthony with mania, aggravated by intemperance (187/1574) from Belgrave Gate, had a son whose avid determination to remove his father from the asylum, was ultimately successful after a fortnight of treatment. Gottfried (205/148) was a draughtsman working at the Brush Works Electrical Engineers in Loughborough, after having a funny turn at work he was admitted to the asylum, but after 6 days was placed into the care of his friends, who took him home to Switzerland. Edward (191/2799) from Earl Shilton performed the great escape, after just 19 days as a patient, by managing to elude one of the attendants when returning from farm work. He must have remained unfound for the statutory period of 14 days.

These exceptionally short stays of less than a month were hardly likely to have been a miracle cure. Accepting that mental illness usually requires a longer period of recovery than some other medical conditions, then over two thousand patients were quite quickly able to see the light at the end of the tunnel & whose time as an asylum patient lasted less than a year. Four patients stayed in the asylum for exactly a year – they were John (186/1310) 10th December 1852 to 10th December 1853 - David (190/2539) 13th August 1864 to 13th August 1865 - Elizabeth (191/2801) 27th January 1869 to 27th January 1870 & William (199/5043) 24th February 1890 to 24th February 1891.

Not all patients were as fortunate as those who required treatment for a year or less. Yet, a high number of other patients even though they did take longer than others to recover, they were not 'in' forever & or were so markedly 'cured' or 'relieved' of their mental conditions that they too were able to return to their former lives. Three hundred & twenty six stayed for over a year, 368 for over 2 years, 323 for over 3 years, 254 for over 4 years, 221 for over 5 years and finally 171 for over 6 years.

Trying to establish accurate statistics of what proportion of the patients were actually cured was essentially quite problematical. The admission registers coupled with the case books did help to give more defined histories for several patients, but the final entries within the case books themselves, often left specific patients being absolutely anywhere. Records of release are quite complex, as some appear to refer to a change in patient status, from for example, charity to private class, rather than their actual release. Within all the admissions & readmissions within the County Asylum itself, (which does not within these specific statistics include the idiots or imbeciles), there were almost three thousand incidences of cure & potentially the ability & or opportunity to return to former lives. Inevitably, for a few any subsequent readmissions, would lead to an individual patient's death within the asylum. Just 81 patients tragically had to receive treatment for more than 10 years. Nine patients were inmates for over 40 years. These patients who had been inmates for prolonged periods, within the asylum, were the exception to the general pattern of length of stay. In terms of total life experience within the asylum, just over two and a half thousand, were either finally cured or relieved enough to be sent back to their previous lifestyles and 2486 patients died within the asylum walls.

Photograph of a patient at the time of admission and a subsequent photograph at the time of recovery. Asylum Casebooks courtesy of ROLLR.

Conclusion

Gallons of ink, hundreds of pens, reams of paper bound in journals or registers, hours of human time, spent both in thought & activation of a writing tool, have allowed us to open, the once securely locked doors and go through the gates into the Leicestershire & Rutland Lunatic Asylum, which was open to patients for seventy years. The most enlightening hand written records were the Case Notes. Initially, a high percentage of illiterate incoming patients must have sat there in awe of the man with the quill pen & inkpot. The intention was always that the records should be as complete as possible & an incredible amount of detective work must have taken place to uncover missing details on patients which included trying to discover who patients actually were & who they were chargeable to. The quantity of letters to & fro must have been phenomenal, before communication by telegram & telephone became available. The onset of photography would of course have helped when identifying certain patients.

After inclusion of various patient details, the case book entries were read by the Lunacy Commissioners who inspected the asylum, the Justices of the Peace who ran it, and the poor law officers who paid for the inmates' maintenance. One wonders what effect all these very official readers had on the initial script content. Matilda (197/4617) from Market Harborough had needlessly complained that the writer was not treating her well in 1885. Other patients defined as 'probably prostitutes' Maria (211/46), 'a ne'er do well' Mabel (210/35) or 'the most grotesque little idiot it is possible to imagine.' Sarah (190/2462) did not perhaps fair so well within the records.

The Leicestershire & Rutland Lunatic Asylum was well run & able to offer restorative benefits, which were essentially otherwise often unavailable, even to the most well-meaning families. The treatments on offer were then wide and where possible all encompassing. For the horrendously, deliriously ill, the asylum became both 'the place of safety' & a hospital still retaining its positive focus of optimum care, even when it was over full, with both curable & incurable patients. It could also ensure that at least every patient had access to the common necessities of life & at the same time significantly lighten the load for many otherwise highly stressed family networks, especially those with a congenitally handicapped offspring. For those who arrived underfed as paupers, dressed in virtual rags then - A life with virtual guaranted employment in the workshops, the laundry, in the gardens or out on the farm, with weekly dances, sport, country walks and an asylum virtual variety show of various entertainments plus three good meals a day must have been an experience of heaven on earth.

Many discovered information about themselves & their former lives, which had the potential to help those patients lead to a much happier life on the other side of the walls. Robert a saddler from Cottesmore was selected employment as an integral part of his treatment, which could have influenced his choice of employment when leaving the asylum: -

> 'For some weeks prior to his discharge he was employed in agricultural pursuits out of doors and tho' a saddler by trade and consequently accustomed to a sedentary life, he proved himself a very good workman with the spade and was of great use in assisting to double dig a piece of ground in a field attached to the asylum for the purpose of growing potatoes. The benefit he derived from being thus employed in the open air he himself stated to be very great - and he expressed great reluctance to return to his own trade which he said had never agreed with him.' (185/663)

It appears from attempts to track him on the following 1851 Census, that Robert may have become a labourer & was no longer recorded as being a saddler. Taking just a small selection of patients from the first surviving case book, who were recorded as either 'cured' or 'relieved', and tracking them (with several matching details) on the same Census as Robert the saddler, then patients were not forever detained. The true triumph of the Institution, must be the victory of the following men getting to back to where they themselves must have felt that they belonged – Joseph (185/592) the cork cutter from Leicester - William (185/589) back as a master carpenter in Loughborough - Joseph (185/579) back as an agricultural labourer in Braunstone - Thomas (185/795) back as an Angora stocking making in Loughborough - Thomas (185/687) was still an inn keeper & was well enough to have moved to a new inn in Nottingham - Thomas (185/603) was still a brick maker in Ripley - John (185/617) was living with his family at his father-in-laws a watchmaker, but is still a surgeon & has two more children - Thomas (185/873) was still a framesmith in Earl Shilton.

This victory was enabled through the man in charge, the Superintendent, who was an incredible multi-tasker of his era. At the same time that he was ensuring the patients & staff were performing as best as they were able, his actions & decisions were being scrutinised by the Commissioners for Lunacy, with all there new rules & guidelines to be strictly adhered to. There were also the very necessary needs of the individuals within the walls - to be diagnosed & treated, to be nursed, to rest & sleep, to be fed, to be watered, to be bathed, to be kept warm, to be clothed & to be given access to activities which would aid recovery. The positive attitude appeared to be directed to all of the patients & even for the congenitally incurable there was a very forward thinking approach. Everything possible was done to make sure the duration of treatment for the 'idiot' & 'imbecile' was time well spent within the asylum walls.

The innovations of the 19th Century must also have had a significant influence on the asylum. The increased use of vaccinations or inoculations, to prevent disease was also evident, especially in the case of David a needle maker's delusion from Loughborough: -

> 'Today he says he cannot help making a wine says he has got a dog in his stomach which is jumping about & when asked how the dog got there & whether he swallowed it he replies that he thinks it must have been inoculated there says he wishes a million times he had never been born that he feels "electrified" - (205/120)

The introduction of telegrams enabled relatives to have more immediate contact with asylum patients & vice versa. Far more patients must have travelled to & from the asylum via the ever-growing railway systems rather than by horse driven vehicles. The new road surfacing, for all the up and coming motor vehicles did unfortunately influence the mental health of Frances (212/112) from Gilmorton, 'A steam roller has been at work outside her house the noise which has aggravated her condition.' The introduction of electricity must have brightened the asylum's darker hours & improved health & safety standards. The last person to see the escaped patient Arthur (206/52) in 1907 was the assistant electrician. There were also the new technological devices such as the skiagraphs (early X-Rays) & photographs. In 1900 when Sarah arrived the doctors deemed it necessary to take skiagraphs (early X-rays, the copies are still within the case books).

'Skiagraphs were lately taken of this patients left hand & foot which show an interesting condition of the bones especially in the hand. The patient much objected to the process at first - being under the impression that her limbs were going to be amputated. In the left hand the extra digit comes between the ring finger & the little finger it is smaller than either of these is slightly webbed to the, little finger.' (203/6119)

To ensure the smooth running of the asylum & to guarantee that all these patients' needs were met, the superintendent had to continually assess the asylum's finances. His patients gave tremendous support to him; in the way many of them worked their treatment days away for the good of the asylum & themselves. The three working environments most referred to within the patient case notes were the farm & gardens, mainly for the men, and the laundry mainly for women patients. The farm or laundry would probably have not been able to function, without the patients being amongst the work force. In May 1877, patients working in the painter's shop were actually painting the woodwork & window panes of the asylum itself under the charge of one of the attendants & Thomas a painter from Hinckley eventually spent four to five days a week painting and ornamenting the Housekeeper's apartments. Before George (185/794) from Leicester left the asylum he was employed in the garden, where he supplied the place of a regular labourer and saved the institution considerably. Having an occupation within the hospital, not only benefited the patient in facilitating his own recovery, but he was also of great value to the asylum itself in balancing its books.

The Superintendent's detailed journals really do enlighten us to life within the asylum. The journal's prime task appears to be, that no dastardly deed was covered up, even if it was the non-performance of the local waterworks company. There were such things as details of any special purchases like the Superintendent's new desk, and any special entertainments organised for the patients. There were not just the promenades around the asylum, the walks into the countryside and unaccompanied excursions into Leicester, which he recorded. Another inclusion within the same Journal also includes record of a trip down to London by a group of five patients, who were taken down by train to visit the Crystal Palace in 1855.[66] One of the most amazing inclusions (included again in this publication) in the Superintendent's Journal, in June 1885 will always be: -

> 'Nevertheless on the 2nd inst in the afternoon, Not one male patient was in bed, in the wards, or even in the airing courts – That is every individual male patient was free & beyond lock & key – and it may be doubted whether this ever occurred before in any Asylum.'[67]

With the superintendent at the helm a tremendous camaraderie must have developed between members of staff, between patients & between both staff & patients. Patients would often helpfully very accurately report on other patients' epileptic attacks. Annie (202/5808) from Shepshed was civil and quietly behaved & constituted herself as guardian of two or three weaker patients in her ward. Patients would often assist nurses or attendants when other patients attacked them. Many patients developed strong companionships with other patients or staff. When William (197/4600) originally of 'no fixed abode' had recovered he was accompanied to the station by the Head Attendant & given

---

66   Superintendent's Journal DE3533-83

67   Superintendent's Journal DE3533-86

a ticket for Manchester. Historical research of the mentally ill within Leicestershire during the 19th Century, enlightens us to the incredible numbers of mentally ill people being transported throughout the United Kingdom, from one location to another, for a variety of reasons.

There are several entries within the casebooks, emphasising various patients' gratitude, for the care that they had been given whilst they were patients within the asylum, regardless of where they had originated. A harness maker from Tilton on the Hill admitted with 'impulsive mania' declared, 'that we are all angels to him because of our kindness.' (201/5477) The kindness they received, during their treatment could perhaps be likened to the support of a bandage or sling. Henry (185/596) a rector from Whissendine, presented the chaplain with a very handsome prayer book. Another Henry (187/1718) a painter from Leicester, 'painted three very ornamental chip tables, which he left as memorials of both his skill' and the staff's kindness. A maltster named George (185/639) from Melton Mowbray, left with much regret and promised to come back & visit the staff. Mary Ann (185/671) a servant from Knaptoft who recovered well, was most anxious to do everything in her power as some recompense for the benefit she had derived from the Institution. For most the biggest gain attained was reclamation of their self-respect.

The later case books with photographs from 1893 really help to put us now in the picture, with many of the later admissions having a second photograph, which from their improved appearance, was taken assumedly when the patient had recovered or was about to be released. New terminologies also wend their way into the records, the 'menopause' 1899 and twice the term 'breakdown' used in 1903 (211/116) & 1907 (206/64). Within the asylum's all encompassing seventy years of treating patients, many were admitted from such horrendous, financial or experiential social circumstances that breakdowns were perhaps inevitable. The guiding principle of to cure & not detain was though never lost, within an asylum that was often virtually bursting at the seams with patients.

Through its statistical success of virtually curing or noticeably relieving over two thousand patients within less than a year of their treatment, this incredible accomplishment helped to keep beds free so that many other seriously, mentally ill individuals could also experience the benefit of an asylum cure too. A key to the open door of life had not been required, due to the forward thinking attitudes of the Superintendent, his immediate staff and all the other individuals or groups directly involved in the successful running of the asylum. The time spent within the Asylum had allowed patients to both be cured and also to be given enough support to take a significant role in curing themselves. By taking a major part in their own cure, it had enabled them to have more mental resources, to sustain their recovery when returning to the big outside world and becoming once again a sane member of society.

Photographs of Patients getting better. Asylum Casebooks courtesy of ROLLR.

Primary Sources

Salaries & Wages March 1849-Dec 1862 DE3533-94

Medical Superintendent's Journal & Report Book DE3533-

83 from Sept 1853 to Jan1862
84 from Jan 1862 to Dec 1870
85 from Jan 1871 to 1880
86 from June 1880 to Sept 1884
87 from Oct 1884 to Dec 1889
88 from Jan 1890 to May 1894
89 from June 1894 to June 1902
90 from July 1902 to Nov 1910

Patient Case Books DE3533-

185-Nos 576-891	Jan 1845 to Aug 1848
186-Nos 892-1314	Aug 1848 to Dec 1852
187-Nos 1315-1733	Dec 1852 to June 1856
188-Nos 1734-1972	June 1856 to Sept 1858
189-Nos 1973-2269	Sept 1858 to May 1861
190-Nos 2270-2566	May 1861 to Jan 1865
191-Nos 2567-2838	Jan 1865 to March 1868
192-Nos 2839-3088	March 1868 to Jan 1870
193-Nos 3089-3395	Jan 1870 to Aug 1873
194-Nos 3396-3740	Aug 1873 to April 1877
195-Nos 3741-4105	April 1877 to Sept 1880
196-Nos 4106-4404	Sept 1880 to Aug 1883
197-Nos 4401-4799	Aug 1883 to Oct 1887 Nos 4401 to 4404 Used Twice
198-Nos 4800-5000	Oct 1887 to Oct 1889
199-Nos 5001-5201	Oct 1889 to Aug 1891
200-Nos 5202-5402	Aug 1891 to March 1893
201-Nos 5403-5603	March 1893 to April 1895 Nos 5604 to 5753 missing
202-Nos 5754-5903	July 1896 to Dec 1897 Nos 5904 to 6055 missing
203-Nos 6056-6205	April 1899 to Dec 1900

From this point patients identified by page number only.

204 Male patients only from Dec 1900 to Aug 1903
205 Male patients only Aug 1903 to Jan 1906
206 Male patients only March 1906 to Sept 1908
210 Female patients only Dec 1900 to Aug 1903
211 Female patients only Aug 1903 to Feb 1906
212 Female patients only Feb 1906 to July 1908
213 Female patients only Aug 1908 to Oct 1908 (The case books continue from this date when the last patients had left but it is assumed that the case books continued to be used in the new asylum).

Registers of Admissions, Discharges, Transfers & Deaths with associated records May 1837 – March 1896 DE3533/145
Registry of Admissions, Register of Patients (pauper) May 1837 – March 1896 DE3533/145 Patients Dec 1837 – Aug 1879 DE3533/147

Charity Case Books DE3533-
217 –Nos 1 to 301 Nov 1839 to Sept 1888
218 – Nos 301 to 469 Sept 1888 to 1908

DE3533-9A Asylum House Visitors Book
Leicestershire & Rutland Lunatic Asylum 1869 Annual Report
Leicestershire & Rutland County Medical Journals LRO DE3533-277/278
Leicestershire & Rutland Lunatic Asylum. Rules for the General Management of the Institution with Prefactory Remarks by the Committee of Vusutors I.S. Crossley Leicester 1849

Secondary Sources

Leicestershire's Lunatics – The Institutional care of Leicestershire's Lunatics during the Nineteenth Century H G Orme W H Brock Leicestershire Museums & Art Galleries 1987 ISBN 085022 227 3

Draft article accepted for publication in International Journal of Law & Psychiatry – The Asylum, the Workhouse, and the Voice of the Insane Poor in Nineteenth Century by Peter Bartlett 1993 L:362.61 10/01

Australian Geographic No 14 April-June 1989 Leech Mania Graeme Sims

The Asylum Gardens. Photograph Courtesy of University of Leicester Archives.

Illustrations

Various individual photographs are taken from the later Case Notes Records of patients who recovered after treatment in the Leicestershire & Rutland Lunatic Asylum. DE3533-203-205-206 Individual identities have been withheld. Courtesy of the Record Office for Leicestershire, Leicester & Rutland at Wigston Magna.

James Murray (the only patient whose full name is given) Etching of the Leicestershire & Rutland Lunatic Asylum January 1890 Courtesy of the University of Leicester Archives ULA/IMA2/2.

Early drawing of the Asylum in 1849 by T Wilson is reproduced from an engraving by H Adlard to be used in Annual Reports Courtesy of the University of Leicester Archives.

Photograph (two) of Fielding Johnson Building - Stewart Collection - Courtesy of the Record Office for Leicestershire, Leicester & Rutland at Wigston Magna.

Photograph of Superintendent's House - Stewart Collection - Courtesy of the Record Office for Leicestershire, Leicester & Rutland at Wigston Magna.

Photograph of Superintendent's Office - Stewart Collection - Courtesy of the Record Office for Leicestershire, Leicester & Rutland at Wigston Magna.

Photograph of a stack of the Asylum Case Books taken at Courtesy of the Record Office for Leicestershire, Leicester & Rutland at Wigston Magna.

Photograph of an unused entry sheet within the case books taken by Courtesy of the Record Office for Leicestershire, Leicester & Rutland at Wigston Magna.

Photograph of letter written by one of the patients (206/78) still within the case books taken at Courtesy of the Record Office for Leicestershire, Leicester & Rutland at Wigston Magna.

Photograph of doctor's entry sheet within the case books (196/4234) taken by Courtesy of the Record Office for Leicestershire, Leicester & Rutland at Wigston Magna.

Photographs of Wards - Stewart Collection - Courtesy of the Record Office for Leicestershire, Leicester & Rutland at Wigston Magna.

Photograph of a snow plough at the asylum - Stewart Collection - Courtesy of the Record Office for Leicestershire, Leicester & Rutland at Wigston Magna.

Photograph of Dr Rothsay C. Stewart one of the former Medical Superintendents - Stewart Collection - Courtesy of the Record Office for Leicestershire, Leicester & Rutland at Wigston Magna.

Photograph of medications for patients taken from Case Books by Courtesy of the Record Office for Leicestershire, Leicester & Rutland at Wigston Magna.

The north-east quadrangle of the Asylum, which would have been used as an airing court for female clients. 1920's photographs - Courtesy of the University of Leicester Archives.

Photographs of the Gardens - Stewart Collection -Courtesy of the Record Office for Leicestershire, Leicester & Rutland at Wigston Magna.

Photograph of the Chapel - Stewart Collection - Courtesy of the Record Office for Leicestershire, Leicester & Rutland at Wigston Magna.

Photograph of the Assembly Hall - Stewart Collection - Courtesy of the Record Office for Leicestershire, Leicester & Rutland at Wigston Magna.

Photograph of the staff's dramatic performance - Stewart Collection - Courtesy of the Record Office for Leicestershire, Leicester & Rutland at Wigston Magna.

Photograph of the Recreation Room Christmas 1890's - Stewart Collection - Courtesy of the Record Office for Leicestershire, Leicester & Rutland at Wigston Magna.

Photograph of haymakers probably close to the asylum itself & not at the Newtown Unthank Farm - Stewart Collection - Courtesy of the Record Office for Leicestershire, Leicester & Rutland at Wigston Magna.

Aerial photograph of the Fielding Johnson Building taken during the early 1930 FG1/3/96 Courtesy of the University of Leicester Archives.

Early photograph of Fielding Johnson Building c1922 University of Leicester Archives Courtesy of the ULA/FG1/3/78.

Photograph of the library (Probably after asylum's closure) - Stewart Collection - Courtesy of the Record Office for Leicestershire, Leicester & Rutland at Wigston Magna.